영어로 읽는 먼나라 이웃나라 9

Korea

D1534485

영어로 읽는 먼나라 이웃나라 제9권 우리나라

이원복 글·그림 | 은정 · 루이스최 옮김

1판 1쇄 인쇄 2008. 12. 04. | 1판10쇄발행 2009. 5 . 30. | 발행처 김영사 | 발행인 박은주 | 등록번호 제406-2003-036호 | 등록일자 1979. 5. 17. | 경기도 파주시 교하읍 문발리 출판단지 515-1 우편번호 413-756 | 마케팅부 031)955-3100, 편집부 031)955-3250, 팩시밀리 031)955-3111 | 저작권자 ⓒ 2008, 이원복 | 이 책의 저작권은 저자에게 있습니다. 서면에 의한 저자와 출판사의 허락없이 내용의 일부를 인용하거나 발췌하는 것을 금합니다. | COPYRIGHT ⓒ 2008 by Rhie, Won-Bok All rights reserved including the rights of reproduction in whole or in part in any form. Printed in KOREA | 값은 표지에 있습니다. | ISBN 978-89-349-3236-9 77910 | 좋은 독자가 좋은 책을 만듭니다. | 김영사는 독자 여러분의 의견에 항상 귀 기울이고 있습니다. | 독자의견 전화 031)955-3200 | 홈페이지 www.gimmyoung.com, 이메일 bestbook@gimmyoung.com

영어로 읽는 **먼나라 이웃나라**

Korea

이원복 글·그림 | 은정·루이스 최 옮김

Won-bok RHIE

우리나라

9

김영사

CONTENTS

Foreword

Introduction _____8

1
Neighbors but Strangers:
Korea, China and Japan _____13

2
The Korean People _____ 61

3
The Successes and
Tribulations of the Koreans _____ 147

4
The Long and Treacherous
Road to Reunification _____ 204

FOREWORD

During the mid-19th century, geographer and cartographer Kim Jungho mapped the entire Korean peninsula for the first time in Korean history. If what Kim Jungho created at that time was the first "land map" of Korea, I would like this book to serve as an original "mind map" of the Korean consciousness. Unlike a "land map," however, that objectively delineates the earth's surface, the "mind map" in this book represents my own subjective views. I expect that there may be some who would disagree with my views, but I welcome any constructive discussions on the "mind map" of Korean society and its people portrayed in this book.

It has been some time since Korea, once known as the "hermit kingdom," emerged from obscurity and transformed itself into an economic powerhouse. Unfortunately, however, despite its status as the 11th largest trading nation in the world, Korea continues to be misunderstood by the outside world, which tends to pass judgment on the country solely based on the manifestations of the Korean attitude, but without taking into account the mindset that drives that very attitude. In fact, to a foreigner, Korea is an enigma, and it is often difficult, for example, to distinguish Korea from China or Japan. I believe this is partly attributable to the dearth of English language materials on Korea and its society and people. It is my hope that the English edition of this book will help such an audience better understand the inner workings of the Korean mindset and spark more interest in Korea. It is also my hope that this book will help young overseas Koreans in establishing their identities as people of Korean descent and in understanding what it means to "be Korean," especially in this day and age.

This is a meaningful book to me, as it is the latest addition to an existing 8-volume series of books on a number of European countries and Japan which I started working on more than 20 years ago. You may be curious as to why it took so long for me to work on *Korea Unmasked*, but, paradoxically, looking outwards before looking inwards gave me the perspective to objectively portray Korea in this book. It is, however, no surprise that *Korea Unmasked*, the latest to be published among the above series of books, is the first to be translated into English. This is so because, as I mentioned above, I believe there is a great need for a book like this that will help outsiders explore the inner workings of the Korean mindset and better understand Korean society and its people.

Korea is a fascinating and dynamic country worthy of a more in-depth look. You are invited to explore further and, through this book, I look forward to being your guide.

Won-bok Rhie

Introduction

* 2001 Korean National Office of Statistics

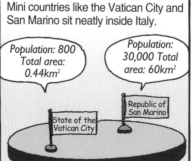

According to the World Bank, there are 229 countries in existence,

among which legitimate data is available for 211.

So, it's probably safe to say there are around 200 countries.

The World Bank classifies these countries into three major groups.

Low-income Per capita GNI US$ 755 or less	
Mid-income Per capita GNI US$756-$9,265	
High-income Per capita GNI US$9,266 or more	

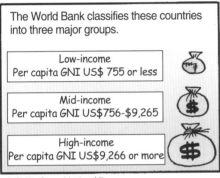

* GNI : Gross National Income

Count them, 50 high-income countries.

Those countries do pretty well for themselves.

Korea reached the US$10,000 per capita GNI level in 1995, joining the illustrious group of high-income countries.

However, due to the impact of the Asian financial crisis in 1997, which caused the value of the U.S. Dollar to sharply appreciate against the Korean Won, Korea's per capita GNI dropped to US$8,490.

Korea slipped to a mid-income nation.

But, Korea has repaid the loans constituting the bailout package from the International Monetary Fund (IMF) early and it's back on track.

Undoubtedly, Korea will rejoin the ranks of high-income countries in no time.

In fact, Korea's doing pretty well for itself as the 11th largest trading nation in the world.

Throughout this book, we'll be comparing Korea to other countries.

Which countries? The 50 high-income countries at the head of the pack.

Excluded from the scope of our comparison are those countries with the majority of their people suffering from poverty.

huff huff

huff

huff

For instance, when we say "Korea recorded the fastest economic growth in the world,"

Korea

we're comparing Korea to the 50 high-income countries,

not the 200 some countries across the planet.

Country A   Country C

Country   Kuwait

Country

Burundi

Saudi Arabia

Why do we make this distinction? There are a lot of small countries out there.

During the 70s and 80s, Korea recorded an economic growth of 10% or more annually.

GNP 100 billion dollars

10 billion dollars

1974   1983

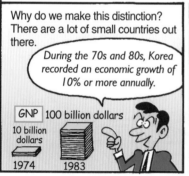

Some countries might have posted higher growth rates.

Our growth rate was much higher!

70 million dollars

5 million dollars

This point should be made clear from the outset in order to avoid any confusion.

This book's incorrect.

Korea Unmasked

Another reason for limiting the scope of our comparison is because we want to compare ourselves to those who are ahead of us and learn from them.

I... must... keep... up!

What's the point in comparing ourselves to countries that are way behind?

I've come far so shall I take a break?

KOR

Having made this point clear, let's begin!

We're only taking into account the 50 high-income nations in our comparisons!

Neighbors but Strangers:
Korea, China and Japan

As we discussed before, there are about 200 countries out there.

All of these countries co-exist with their neighboring countries.

Isolated island country here. Hello?

You still have neighbors, right?

Among all these countries, you won't find neighbors more different than Korea, China and Japan.

Ni hao!

Annyeongha seyo?

Konnichiwa!

People say neighboring countries England, France and Germany are very different.

Good morning!

Bon jour!

Guten tag!

But look... Their people believe in the same God and Jesus Christ.

Jesus... The Virgin Mary!

England   France   Germany

They all use the same letters, the alphabet.

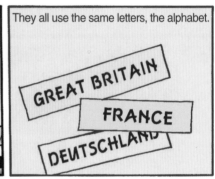

GREAT BRITAIN

FRANCE

DEUTSCHLAND

They all use forks and knives.

The three East Asian countries, on the other hand, don't even share these basic traits.

Let's look at these countries from the perspective of religion. China is said to be the land of Confucianism.

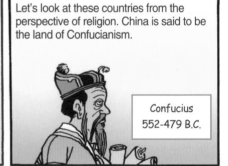

Confucius
552-479 B.C.

Among the hundreds of religions in China, however, Confucianism has become an underlying social and ethical philosophy, not a practicing religion.

How big a country is China?

In fact, more people have turned to Taoism, meditating for happier lives and tranquility.

Please let me earn a lot of money.

After communism overtook China, the Cultural Revolution greatly destroyed Confucian traditions.

waaa

Red Guard

Confucius is an enemy of the worker!

waaa

Turning to Japan, when Buddhism was first introduced,

practitioners of *Shinto*, the native religion of Japan, were anything but pleased.

Just say no to imported religion!

Prince Shotoku (574-622 A.D.) was the big man in Japan at the time.

Religious wars will end up killing us all.

He proclaimed freedom of religion.

Believe in whatever religion you want.

No fighting over religion!

Therefore, Confucianism, Shintoism and Buddhism had no choice but to co-exist with each other in Japan.

Hodge-podge of religions!

Confucian Analects say be faithful!

Goddess Amaterasu!*

Buddhist goddess of mercy!

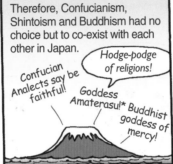

* Amaterasu-O-mi-kami : Sun goddess in Japanese founding myth

Buddhism was the main religion before the Meiji Restoration in 1868.

Shinto	Buddhism	Confucianism
National identity	Main religion	Governing ideology

But in Korea, the Joseon* Dynasty (1392-1910) kings revered Confucianism, adopting it as the country's official religion, but they suppressed Buddhism.

Oppress Buddhism!

Revere Confu-cianism!

* Previously known as Choson

And Korea became the most Confucianism-centered country in the world.

Confucius says...

Mencius says...

Christianity spread after Korea's liberation from Japan in 1945.

Repent! Believe in the Lord and obtain salvation!

Amen!

Surpassing Buddhism, Christianity has become the No.1 religion in Korea with 35% of the population professing to be believers.

Others

It's a sight that cannot be seen anywhere else in Asia: tens of thousands of churches nationwide.

Those are all churches?

The religious manifestations in Korea are entirely different from those in Japan and China.

We're still a socialist country.

Buddhist goddess of mercy

Amen!

Religion's no big deal.

China

Korea

Japan

Although the Koreans, Chinese and Japanese all belong to the same Chinese-character-using cultural sphere,

中國
China

韓國
Korea

東洋三國*

日本
Japan

* 3 countries of the East

the Chinese use a simplified version of Chinese characters,

氣→气
從→从
車→车
歲→岁

the Japanese use two kinds of alphabets, *Hiragana* and *Katakana*

Katakana

バーゲンセール

Hiragana

お客さま
ありがとう
こざいました

and the Koreans use *Hangeul*, which was promulgated by King Sejong in 1446.

사은 대축제*
창고정리
대세일

* Bargain sale

Not only the written but also the spoken languages couldn't be more different.

Ling ling,
Wo ai ni!*

Yeong-ja ssi,
dangshineul
saranghaeyo!*

Eikosan, watashiwa kimi
o aishiteru!*

Zheadema?**

Jeongmal?**

Hontoni?**

* I love you.
** Really?

The English, French and Germans are supposed to be so different, but, at least, they all sleep on beds!

ZZZ

Likewise, the Chinese sleep on beds and sit in chairs.

囍

Meanwhile, the Japanese sleep on *tatami* mats,

while the Koreans sleep on a warm heated *ondol* floor covered with laminated paper.

Oh... oh... that hits the spot... This heated floor is so soothing!

The traditional clothing worn by people in these three countries are also unique.

Even the length of their chopsticks differ.

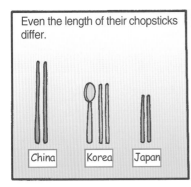

The Chinese eat a lot of deep-fried food.

They use long chopsticks as tools to pick up these foods.

Can't get oil on me. Must not get burned.

Meat having been rare in Korea, hot soup was made with small portions of meat and then shared by many in smaller servings.

So, the Koreans have always used chopsticks and a spoon in tandem.

Can't eat soup with chopsticks, can we?

slurpp

Only the Koreans use a spoon to eat rice.

Because chopsticks are only auxiliary utensils, the Koreans don't need long chopsticks like the Chinese.

In Japan, rice used to be precious and rare so people mixed various cereals when preparing meals.

kaoliang grain   millet

Adding cereals made the rice less gluti-nous. It was not easy for the Japanese to handle the slippery rice with chopsticks.

Crumble

Naturally, they brought the bowls close to their faces and shoveled in the rice.

Shorter chopsticks were more convenient.

These chopsticks are too long.

The Japanese still bring rice bowls close to their mouths. It's a hard habit to break.

My! He eats holding his rice bowl to his mouth!

Wow! He's eating with a spoon!

Although they are neighboring countries, Korea, Japan and China couldn't be more different.

It is hard to tell them apart just by their looks.

You're Chinese, right?

No, Korean!

Ways of thinking, value systems and lifestyles... We have nothing in common!

大中華 世界的中心

HUB KOREA !

脫亞入歐, 脫歐入亞?

What could be the reason?

Put simply, England, France and Germany have incessantly interacted and warred with each other.

Pow! Bam!

They've mixed and matched... throughout history.

England

Germany

France

They share common historical, cultural and social traits.

England

France

Germany

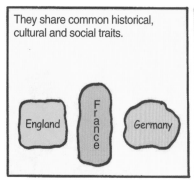

It's fair to say that the Koreans, Chinese and Japanese have also incessantly interacted with each other, but only to a certain degree.

To a greater degree, each country shut itself off from the others, forging its own unique history.

Don't...don't... No...no... Don't even look at those savages!

Just leave me alone!

Let's live amongst ourselves.

China

Korea

Japan

China considered itself as the center of the world.

中華

It paid little attention to Korea and Japan, which it considered to be remote, border countries.

Korean peninsula

Ever since the Mongol invasions, and up to the Ching Dynasty, various minority people have ruled China.

Since the T'ang Dynasty, the Chinese have embraced minorities with a policy of tolerance and cosmopolitanism.

Feisty little fellers. Come to daddy .

They put all the minority races into one big melting pot and stirred them into one culture centered on the Han culture.

mi   no   ni   ties

Han culture

They brought all this together into one huge, unified culture.

We're all Chinese!

Time: 18th century... China was culturally far ahead of the West.

Wooo!

Ahhhh!

The Chinese weren't shaking in their boots because of foreign cultures. In fact, they let other cultures in without much concern.

You ask, "Shall we accept the cultures of savages?"

"Let them in!" I say. Our culture will soak them in like a sponge!

They believed that Chinese culture was the mainstream world culture. They were very proud and confident.

Culture of savages

Chinese culture

Let's turn the mike over to historian Arnold Toynbee.*

Mmm-hum... Yes... Yes... After the Han Dynasty... You see... The Chinese discarded their bellicosity and chose peace.

* Arnold Joseph Toynbee (1899~1975) : England

The concept of unity and peace forms the core of China's spirit, and cosmopolitanism the spirit of the Chinese.

Unity

Cosmopolitanism

Peace

However, because this 'unity and peace' was 'peace for unity,'

One China! One World!

Border country

Border

---

border countries like Korea were forced to submit to China.

We are one, I'm telling you!

Border countries that pursued independence faced non-stop Chinese invasions.

You claim independence? I don't think so.

And the main victim of all of this was Korea.

You won't listen to us and want to play alone again?

The Korean peninsula is just a tiny projection on the eastern side of the Chinese mainland.

Up until the early part of the Goryeo* Dynasty (918-1392 A.D.), the Koreans were able to fend off the Chinese.

Fierce!

* Previously known as Koryo

But after the Mongol invasions, the unified China was too much for Korea.

By the time of the Joseon period, Korea was forced to submit to the Chinese policies of 'unity' and 'peace.'

Goodness! I've heard enough already!

Korea agreed to become a vassal country of China on one condition:

All right! I'll call you big brother!

Independence of the Korean peninsula... even if a mere formality...

Keep your nose out of my business!

Let's suppose Korea didn't do this but openly and frequently interacted with the Chinese.

The two people would have mixed, and Korea would have lost its national identity.

Chinese

Koreans

Except for limited diplomatic and trading ties that were absolutely required,

If you're done with your business, go home!

Korea bolted its doors, and its people were prevented from mixing and mingling with foreigners.

Purpose of travel? Denied!

NO!

For 500 years, Korea was isolated... just like an island.

STOP Korea

During those years, Korea developed its own unique culture and customs.

We're different!

What about Japan? They sit alone in the east.

After the failed Mongol invasions,

except in the case of the U.S. occupation after World War II,

Japan has lived without foreign invasions unlike most other Asian countries.

Japan adapted both Korean and Chinese cultures... including Buddhism with open arms.

They absorbed foreign cultures with this unique islander mentality.

Japan developed its own unique culture

that was shaped differently from Korean and Chinese culture.

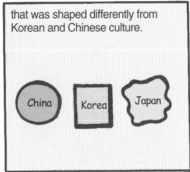

Wars weren't waged against the people,

but between those in power, who were each struggling for the upper hand.

Unlike the Chinese and Koreans, the Japanese lived without fear of a foreign invasion.

Instead of developing a large-scale, masculine culture, the Japanese developed a subtle, delicate and feminine culture.

These countries greatly differ from one another.

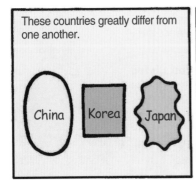

Yet, oddly enough, they share one common trait.

Regardless of the size of their population, they are each a homogeneous people.

I'm Chinese!

I'm Korean!

Me Japanese!

The Chinese think of themselves as the center of the world. Chinese culture = world culture.

For thousands of years, the Chinese have preserved a unified country.

There are 1.3 billion people living in China today. They all consider themselves as Chinese.

Chinese!

Chinese!

Chinese!

Chinese!

Chinese!

Chinese!

The Koreans have suffered for thousands of years from recurring foreign invasions.

Oh, No! Here they come again!

A national consciousness of unity developed as the Koreans came together to fend off foreign aggressors.

Having lived as one people since the Unified Shilla Dynasty (57 B.C. - 935 A.D.), a national spirit of camaraderie binds the Korean people.

We may not get along at times.

But we're still brethren!

The Japanese lived together for thousands of years, enduring many ups and downs.

Boom Bam Pow

Can't we all just get along?

The homogeneous Japanese population consists of 130 million people.

Watashiwa Nihonjin Desu! (I'm Japanese.)

Because of this strong sense of homogeneity and camaraderie, compared to most western countries, it's easier to define the characters and cultures of Asian countries.

The culture and the country are one!

China   Korea   Japan

What is the most important value of each of the three East Asian countries?

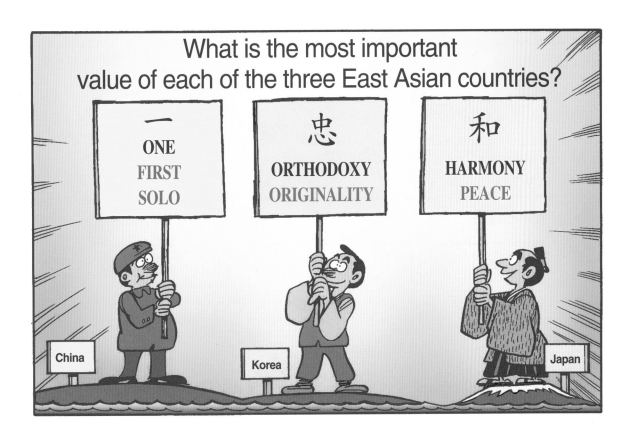

一
ONE
FIRST
SOLO

忠
ORTHODOXY
ORIGINALITY

和
HARMONY
PEACE

China

Korea

Japan

What do the Koreans, Japanese and Chinese each consider to be the most important value?

An essential and irreplaceable value safeguarded by each people.

The most important value

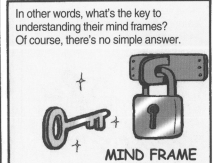

In other words, what's the key to understanding their mind frames? Of course, there's no simple answer.

MIND FRAME

But if there is a one-word answer to this question for each country,

One word!

one would be the answer for the Chinese.

One

一 *

Why **one**? Let me try to explain.

*You're trying to simplify us into this **one**?*

One?

* 'Yi' in Chinese. 'Il' in Korean.

23

As you well know, China is a huge country.

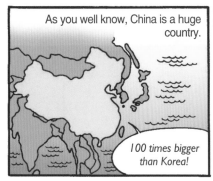

100 times bigger than Korea!

In a country of such size, people with power were bound to sprout up all over the place.

They formed their own countries, and engaged in endless struggles with each other.

Each country attempted to expand its territory by waging war against its neighbors.

Never was there a day without a war.

clash
clash

The people were profoundly devastated, living in fear for their lives and suffering from poverty.

What was the lesson the Chinese learned after suffering through years and years of wars?

All we are saying is give peace a chance! No more wars!

Peace through might! This is only possible if somebody unifies the entire country through strength!

Only with an absolute, untouchable ruler and a strong, unified country could strife be avoided.

Absolute authority and a unified country

were required to achieve peace.

The Chinese realized this after suffering through many years of wars.

Unified country = Peace
Division = War

After Emperor Qin Shi Huangdi (259-210 B.C.) unified China in B.C.221,

B.C. 221

the Chinese struggled to remain as **one**, regardless of the price they had to pay.

Division

Except for certain periods of division, China remained unified for more than 2,000 years.

The Three Kingdoms

Nothern and Southern Dynasties

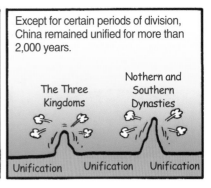

Unification   Unification   Unification

It's hard to find any other country in history that has managed to remain unified for that long.

Although it has been over 1,000 years since the fall of the Roman Empire, which lasted for a millennium,

...China's still unified!

We are the only one in the world.

But, no matter how strong the empire might've been,

China was just too enormous. How was it to govern every nook and cranny?

I'm a King!

Me, too!

Me, three!

Me, four!

China opened its arms, embracing all people living on the Chinese mainland with a cosmopolitan policy.

Stop all your fussing and come to daddy!

It adopted a policy of tolerance and compromise.

Scaring the daylights out of them on one side.

Patting and hugging them on the other.

Under the umbrella of this fundamental philosophy, they used a system of vassalage to keep China unified as **one** country.

My offering...

Under this system of vassalage,

We're not China's little brother.

You are if we say so!

as long as China was recognized as 'big brother,'

China promised autonomy... a status nothing short of independence.

I pledge my allegiance...

I grant you autonomy.

If one accepted its status as a part of China,

China guaranteed self-governance and limited interference in domestic affairs.

In other words, China was at the top of a loose affiliation of border countries.

These border countries would send envoys to China every year packed with tributary gifts, pledging their devotion as loyal vassals.

But don't misunderstand – China wasn't extorting these 'gifts' from these countries.

Because these gifts symbolized devotion, in order to appease these countries,

China would repay its vassals with gifts manyfold.

In Korea, during the Joseon period, the Koreans settled into brown-nosing the man in power.

The overpowering Chinese did interfere with domestic issues to a certain extent.

However, it could be said that Joseon maintained its independence for 500 years because of this vassalage system.

Although the Koreans proudly claim that Korea was an independent country,

from the Chinese point of view, Korea was a part of China.

After the Japanese defeated the Chinese in the Sino-Japanese War,*

Crouching tiger! More like paper tiger!

the first thing the Japanese did was to force China to recognize Joseon's independence from China.

You're an independent country, right?

Uhh... Umm... Yes that's right!

Why were the Japanese so adamant in separating Joseon from China? So that they could invade the Korean peninsula without worrying about China.

Yes... Yes... We are an independent country.

Good! Since this is a matter between two independent countries, stay out of it China!

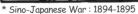
* Sino-Japanese War : 1894-1895

What happened if a country refused to become a vassal country and proclaimed independence from China?

Separate country here!

The result would've been... endless brutal wars without boundaries or limits.

Crack!

This tradition of **oneness** has been China's fundamental policy that continues on to this day.

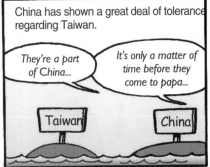

China is one! We're one no matter what!

China

The dissolution of the **one** China only meant strife, chaos and war.

ONE CHINA

The Chinese continue to embrace this belief and will never give up on it.

Immutable fundamental rule

One China

China has shown a great deal of tolerance regarding Taiwan.

They're a part of China...

It's only a matter of time before they come to papa...

Taiwan

China

But it would be a different story if... let's say... Taiwan claims, "We're not part of China. We're independent!"

Taiwan independence!

WHAT!

Taiwan

China

If Taiwan continues to assert its independence,

Taiwan independence!

Impossible!

Taiwan

China has said that it wouldn't hesitate to go to war. This is the fundamental '**One China**' philosophy at work...

War will be your only friend if you continue!

Taiwan

In 1997, the United Kingdom returned Hong Kong to China after 99 years.

Hong Kong

True, the 'one country, two systems' policy is a product of the practical nature and policy of tolerance of China.

We're going to live the way we've always lived.

Sure!

Capitalism / Socialism

But remember... China allows this because Hong Kong has recognized itself as being a part of China... a Chinese territory.

Hong Kong is a Chinese territory!

Of course! Good boy! Now go and play!

Many Islamic people live in the region neighboring Central Asia.

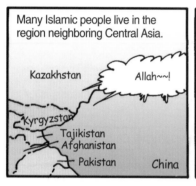

Kazakhstan

Allah~~!

Kyrgyzstan
Tajikistan
Afghanistan
Pakistan
China

They desire independence from China and the formation of a separate Islamic state.

A separate Islamic state!

The Tibetans have also waged a fierce struggle to gain independence.

China forced us to merge in 1950.

We want independence!

Allowing these countries independence would mean their departure from the **oneness** of China.

Independent Country

One China

China would do whatever it takes, using all means necessary, to crush these movements for independence.

crush

*Having even one of these territories leave would mean an end to the civilized world as we know it! The breakdown of our supreme principle — the **oneness** of China. Never! It cannot be done! No! No!*

---

*The end of **one** China! This would lead to chaos and strife! The destruction of lives and property of the Chinese people!*

*A Unified China... Maintaining **One** China is the key to protecting the lives and property of the 1.3 billion people of China!*

This is why China makes such a big deal about being **One**.

The ethnic Koreans* living in China are allowed to speak and run broadcasts in their mother tongue.

But start digging your graves if you even utter the word independence.

* A large number of ethnic Koreans live in China.

28

The Chinese still place this **oneness** on a pedestal.

This doesn't apply to only the territories of China, but also to the people and the culture...

Country

Culture

People

The **One** China, which was unified for 2,000 years, largely consists of the Han people (i.e., the Chinese race)...

Among the 1.3 billion people, 70% come from the same race!

But China also absorbed the 50-some-odd minority people through its policy of inclusion and tolerance.

Minority people

Today, China has the largest population in the world. 1.3 billion!

Although I am ethnically Korean,

I am Chinese indeed.

Although there have been times when China was ruled by minority people,

the cultures of these minorities coalesced into the Han culture, thereby becoming part of the culture of **One** China.

Han culture

Minority people

Chinese

Meanwhile, 30 million Chinese emigrants live in various places around the world.

Even these emigrants unite under the banner of **One** China.

"Wo shi Zhongguoren!"*
(我是中國人)

London Paris Rome LA New York

* I'm Chinese!

This clearly reflects the notion that every Chinese living on the planet is...

One! We're Chinese!

Helsinki

Moscow

Toronto

Reykjavik

Athens

Rio de Janeiro

Johannesburg

Sidney

The 'One Mentality' has tied the country, the people and the culture together as 'one.'

Chinese mainland

Chinese people

Chinese culture

This mentality has been the driving force that propelled China into the ranks of the strongest countries in the world.

This Chinese character '一' means 'one' but it also means 'the best.'

Sinocentrism symbolizes the pride of the Chinese people.

In so many words, they think the Chinese people, culture and, in fact, just about anything Chinese are the best in the world.

Savages to the north

Savages to the east

Savages to the west

Barbarians to the south

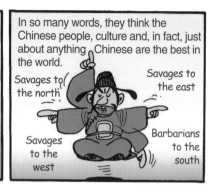

This pride continued despite China having been disgraced by repeated invasions by world powers.

A savage has just broken my nose...

This pride is not just dreamy nostalgic reflections of China's glorious yesteryears...

Yesterday, all my troubles seemed so far away...

It's a confidence that permeates modern day China – a belief that they can be the greatest country, the superpower of the world.

2008 Beijing Olympic Games

Qualified for the 2002 World Cup.

7% economic growth!

Looking good! We're headed for the top!

Things were very different during the latter half of the 19th century. Western powers stepped on the ego of the Chinese. The world community disrespected them.

The Chinese are lazy and filthy!

What did Napoleon have to say after catching a glimpse of China's potential?

Monsieur, don't wake a sleeping lion!

But these European countries, which had only a fraction of China's population, rolled into China with their imperialistic policies and trampled over the country. China was insulted.

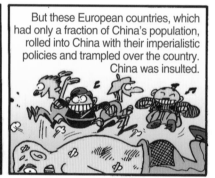

Distinguished and prominent European thinkers and philosophers, people we all know by name, mocked China.

A great country? Are we talking about the same country here?

Turn the mike over to Hegel*...

China is an enormous country that time forgot.

* Hegel : German philosopher

"Although China is an enormous country, nothing has changed for thousands of years. Only China's rulers, not its people, enjoy freedom."

2000 yrs ago   1000 yrs ago   Present

Step up to the mike, Karl Marx*...

China's stagnant... For thousands of years,

its leaders have been replaced but the lower class has never changed.

*K. Marx : German thinker

What did Friedrich Engels* have to say?

They're a very lazy people...

They don't have the will power to last in Asia!

*F. Engels : English thinker

Tell us your thoughts, Max Weber.*

The Chinese are passive and dull.

They lack sympathy and honor!

So tell us what you really think

*M. Weber : German philosopher

The self-indulgent observations of these Western thinkers show that they failed to see the potential power of the oneness of China.

We're so much better.

Armed with modern weapons, the invading imperialistic powers from the West pulverized the Chinese. Falling like dominos, the Chinese did look pitiful.

This is too easy.

Bang

After the dissolution of the Soviet Union...

Russia's financial situation turned sour... despite its status as the largest country in the world.

Russia's economy

In contrast, look at the Chinese. They endured domestic strife between the Communists and the Nationalists... They went through the Cultural Revolution and much more.

Civil war

Cultural Revolution

Now, they have emerged as one of the strongest economic powers in the world.

Isn't this a product of their desire to become the 'best'?

C H I N A

The Americans are moving quickly to arm themselves with a missile defense system (MD).

Missile Defense

Why? They've realized China will be the only superpower that will be able to go against America.

America's main enemy is now China!

Another meaning for the Chinese character '一' is 'solo.'

ONLY ME!

SOLO, ALONE

*'Yi' in Chinese, 'il' in Korean

This also means that the Chinese tend to look out only for themselves.

The Chinese have suffered much throughout their history,

which led the Chinese to only trust themselves and their families.

They could care less about what happened to others.

They became self-centered, looking out only for themselves and their own good.

Devotion? That's hogwash!

Who is the king? It makes no difference to the people! I need to take care of myself.

As mentioned earlier, 1.3 billion people in China and tens of millions of people abroad unite under the banner of '**One** China.'

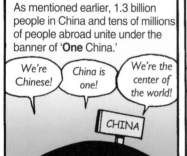

We're Chinese!

China is one!

We're the center of the world!

CHINA

But... and this is a big but... they're a very selfish people at the same time, looking out for only their own well-being and prosperity.

Me!

My kids, my wife!

My family!

Me!

This 'me only' mentality pervades the lives of the Chinese.

China has had a difficult history!

I may have been born in troubled waters but I'm going to die in comfort...

One China... the best culture... the 'me only' mentality...

Thus, the Chinese character '一' represents the values and mentality of the Chinese people.

That's the reason why China's most important value is represented by '一.' Interesting isn't it?

What would be the most important value of the Japanese then?

That's easy. That would be 'wa'.*

* 'Hwa' in Korean

What does wa mean? It means peace and harmony.

Peace and Harmony!

There are many words that contain 'wa'.

和親
1. Friendship

和議
5. Peace negotiation

和解
2. Reconciliation

和好
6. Harmonious

和氣
3. Geniality

和樂
7. Peaceful

和同
4. Unison

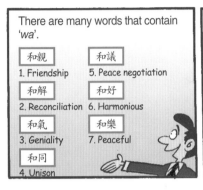

In other words, what all this boils down to is... 'let's live in harmony.'

I ask for your good will...

No... No... I ask for your good will...

How did peace and harmony, wa, become the most important national values to the Japanese?

Japan is an island country.

Tell me something I don't know!

Island countries are characterized by different traits than those of continental and peninsular countries.

Conti-nent

Peninsula

Island

3 sides face the ocean

4 sides face the ocean

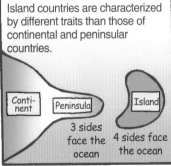

Different ethnic people were constantly at war in continental and peninsular countries...

waaa

wooo

For island countries, the ocean served as a natural barrier against foreign invasions.

Catch me if you can!

Na-na-na-nana!

The greatest danger for island countries didn't come from external threats but from internal struggles.

If an internal war erupted, the people living on the island had nowhere to run.

They would have no choice but to fight each other, spelling the end for all involved.

As early as the 6th century, the Japanese designated *wa* as the highest virtue to be upheld.

As an island country, we must stop internal wars at all cost!

Prince Shotoku (574-622) created Japan's first constitution known as the Constitution of Seventeen Articles.

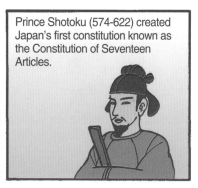

Article One stressed peace and harmony.

Article One

Harmony is to be valued. No fighting!

Waging war inside the island will kill everybody!

Nearly all island countries, not just Japan, consider peace and harmony to be very important.

Let's think about this... What would it take for people living on an island to live in peace and avoid fighting?

First, there would need to be a 'divine figure' worthy of the respect of the people.

What's going on here?

This figure would mediate disputes.

You were right.

Now, I want you to forgive him. Okay?

Why wouldn't there be powerful people in island countries who desire to rise to the top?

Let's say a person like that does gain power.

Divine ruler? Ha! What a load of...

Eh? Who does he think he is?

But if another stronger, tougher person comes to town, another fight would break loose.

Let's go at it!

Endless wars would then engulf the island country just like continental and peninsular countries.

Clash   Clash

To avoid such a tragedy, the people placed a so-called divine ruler at the top who, in actuality, had no real power...

All hail thee!

Instead, another person with real power governed the people.

So two systems coexisted.

Symbolic leader	Real leader

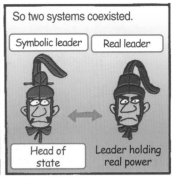

Head of state	Leader holding real power

During the formative period of a country, one leader performs both functions.

Symbolic power

Real power

Because of the special circumstances of island countries, after a long struggle, the structure of power shifts to the dual system.

Reigns   Rules

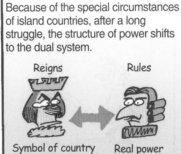

Symbol of country   Real power

In Japan's case, during the early stages of the country, the *tenno* (emperor) reigned and ruled over the country.

Tenno

Imperial Court

Eventually, the *tenno* was reduced to a mere figurehead.

Tenno

National symbol

The *Bakufu* regime ruled the country instead.

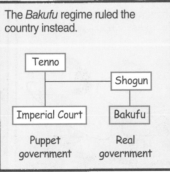

Tenno

Shogun

Imperial Court

Bakufu

Puppet government   Real government

The *Shogun* was, in essence, the emperor, and, for that matter, the real person in charge.

Execute him!

Fellow island country England was like Japan in the beginning. The king was not a mere figurehead.

But the king was eventually stripped of most of his powers.

Symbol of country   Real power

Most of such powers are now vested in the prime minister and a parliament.

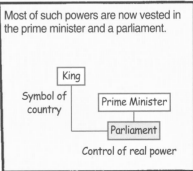

King

Symbol of country

Prime Minister

Parliament

Control of real power

England's Parliament and Japan's *Bakufu* essentially served the same roles.

The *Bakufu* regime was made up of the *bushi** class, which practically ruled Japan.

* Warrior

In England, the local feudal lords that gathered at Parliament constituted the ruling class.

This dual system characterizes the structure of power in island countries.

In order to preserve 'wa', i.e., in order for islanders to live in peace,

it was important for them to avoid conflict.

Without the meeting of the hands, of course, no sound would be produced.

If the hands don't meet... whiff... nothing... zero sound... peace...

It's a surefire way of avoiding confrontations and conflict.

As basic as it sounds... there is no better way to maintain peace than to avoid bumping into each other.

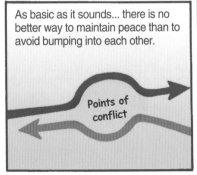

Avoiding conflict in order to preserve *wa*.

This way of thinking is deeply embedded in the psyche and customs of the Japanese.

How is it possible to avoid running into each other?

Well, each person would have to foresee possible points of conflict and take measures to avoid such conflict.

Each person would have to understand what makes the other person tick.

He must be thirsty...

Thoughtful consideration of others, known as *kikubari* in Japanese,

I have an extra can of coke here.

I can't drink both. Would you help me finish it off?

is basic good manners to all Japanese.

If I forced the coke on him, I would've hurt his feelings.

Being considerate of the feelings of others means being amiable and gentle.

I'm all right...

But if it'll help you out, it would be my pleasure.

The Japanese demeanor is grounded in this amiable and gentle disposition... *yasashii*.

Next is the 7th floor.

I know. It's not like I can't count.

The world-renowned cordiality of the Japanese starts here.

Welcome!

The Japanese language follows this temperament—it's smooth and gentle.

I graciously thank you for your continuing concern.

Please, don't mention it. I'm the one who should feel gracious.

The use of rough language, especially curse words, is considered atrocious behavior.

Why I ought to... I ought to...

You could say Japan is Old World when it comes to curse words.

Are you an idiot?!

My God! How can he use such harsh language!

Very, very different from the Koreans...

Yo! You bastard, long time no see!

Goodness! To call a friend a...!

The Japanese try avoiding the use of words that would make their counterparts uncomfortable.

The following scene would be unthinkable for a Japanese:

Hey! You stepped on my foot. You'd better apologize, shouldn't you?

Hey! Did I do that on purpose?

Although the Japanese might be annoyed on the inside, on the outside they would say:

I'm very sorry!

No... No... It was my fault!

The Japanese also avoid the use of words that might provoke others.

So, inevitably there's a difference between what they're thinking and what they're saying.

I never want to see this bozo again...

Let's get together soon!

The *honne* (genuine motives) — *tatemae* (the way things are presented) dichotomy is deeply engrained in Japanese society.

ABC   XYZ

Foreigners have the hardest time understanding this trait.

What you think and say are two different things!

Jekyll and Hyde!

But the other side of the coin is that

Uhh... Great atmosphere... And food's great... great restaurant.

Horrible restaurant! Never ever coming back!

the Japanese don't literally believe each and every word of the other person.

You did a wonderful job of research and this will contribute greatly to this field. However, there are some points that need to be reconsidered...

Instead, they ponder on what might be the other person's real intentions.

Oh man! This research paper is not passing...

Since the Japanese are able to communicate among themselves without difficulty,

You failed to pass.

I flunked...

instead of accusing the Japanese as being a double-faced people, we can understand this as their effort to preserve *wa*.

At least superficially, nobody's feelings would get hurt.

The behavior of the Japanese commonly exhibits this mentality to avoid conflict.

They're very cautious in avoiding physical contact.

When they greet someone, they bow... rarely will you see them shake hands.

Many a Japanese have become flustered when unknowing foreigners offer to shake hands.

If they bump into each other by accident, the bowing fest for forgiveness begins...

Regardless of how close two friends may be, you'll rarely see them hug.

You'll hardly ever see them playfully pat each other as well.

In the eyes of the Japanese, the sight of the Koreans cursing at friends as a greeting and

playfully giving each other body shots must look very strange.

As we discussed, the Japanese are extremely careful about not running into each other.

It doesn't matter how close two friends may be. The boundaries are clear.

It's hard for Koreans to understand the sight of two Japanese friends bowing to each other when saying goodbye.

But the Japanese simply do not encroach upon the territory of another person.

And they don't do anything others might consider burdensome.

Why not stay for dinner while you're here?

Uhh... Umm... I really need to get home!

They seem to all live in their own little capsules.

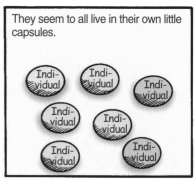

With each person living in his or her own secure world, it would seem hard for them to get together.

You're you!

I'm me!

But, when there's a common goal,

no other people unites better than the Japanese!

Let's raise our department record!

In contrast, the Koreans have very close, intertwined relationships...

Hey! How about some dinner for the guest?

Sure!

Mom!

How intertwined?

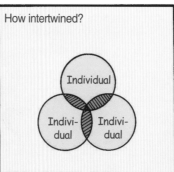

The Koreans commonly run and bump into other people,

I'm busy!

Crash

and the closer they get to people, the more they encroach upon their territories.

The Koreans also consider it perfectly natural for other people to encroach upon their territories.

Obviously, the Koreans and the Japanese have very different mentalities.

The Japanese have no emotions!

The Koreans are ill mannered.

In sum, the Japanese tend to avoid close direct contact with others while the Koreans tend to promote such contact.

The differences between these two countries are exemplified by the ways they approach videogames.

Japanese kids tend to play video games alone.

Sony Playstation... Sega...

Japan is the most advanced country in the world when it comes to creating games that can be played alone.

It falls way behind, however, when it comes to games played with other people such as online games...

Online games? Too much contact with people...

Compared to Japan that has only a relatively small number of online games,

That's very weak for a country that supposedly leads the world in game development...

Korea offers dozens of online games.

Koreans get fired up by the competition.

The tens of thousands of Internet cafes spread across Korea are filled with young persons battling faceless enemies.

I'm going to beat you!

That's why these Internet cafes are exploding!

So, Japan is the most advanced country when it comes to offline games played alone,

whereas Korea is the most advanced country when it comes to online games played with other people.

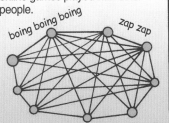

Just by looking at this, don't you get some idea of how different these two countries are?

I can't live alone. I get very bored.

I can't live with many people. Too uncomfortable...

The most important lesson Japanese parents teach their children:

The Japanese avoid conflict with each other as much as possible.

They avoid possible points of conflict by being considerate of the feelings of others and by being nice and friendly.

The Japanese realize that it would be the end for all if they started fighting and quarreling in their confined island country.

They place *wa*, peace and harmony, ahead of other values.

It's an absolute priority.

Thus, you can understand why the Japanese act and think the way they do by understanding the concept of *wa*.

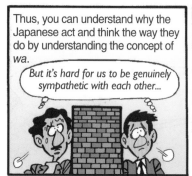

Everything else is then crystal clear.

As discussed earlier, the Chinese consider...

For the Japanese, it's *wa*.

What about the Koreans? Good question!

The answer can be traced to Korea's geographical location, the fact that it's a peninsula!

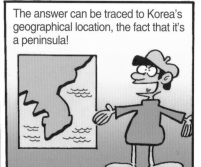

A peninsula is an extension of a continent, surrounded on three sides by water. Right?

A peninsula serves as a natural bridge for continental countries to cross over and sail to islands.

It's a two-way street — Island countries also use the peninsula to cross over into the continent.

Now, everything was just peachy for the Italian peninsula while the Romans were in power.

Nobody dared mess with the Romans.

But after the fall of the Roman Empire, all the European superpowers eyed the peninsula...

Before its unification in 1860, Italy was plagued by war for nearly 1,500 years!

Peninsular countries are strategically important.

This was especially true in the case of Korea.

Continental powerhouse China was in one corner,

while ambitious Japan looking for the continental title was in the other corner.

In addition to these two powerhouses, numerous other foreigners incessantly committed aggressions upon Korea.

The constant invasions and plundering greatly distressed the Koreans.

Their first priority was...

Survival! Here they come again!

For survival, the Koreans had to be ready at all times to fight off foreign aggressors.

The Korean way of life was very wearisome.

Can't let up for even a second.

Frequent foreign invasions result in frequent contact with foreigners,

which significantly increases the probability that different races would mix.

Suppose a particular race mixes with foreigners over a span of thousands of years.

What would happen? The bloodline, its racial identity, would eventually be lost.

If bloods mix, our race will eventually exist no more.

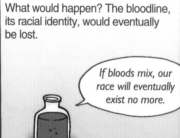

For the sake of preserving their lineage... the Koreans became very exclusionary, discouraging the mixing with other races.

Since you bear the child of a foreign savage, *take your life!*

Look at the countries of the Balkan peninsula. They've suffered for nearly 2,000 years from foreign invaders.

But the people of each country did not mix with others, thereby enabling each such people to eventually survive as an independent race.

❶ Slovenia/Croatia/ Bosnia-Herzegovina/ New Yugoslavia
❷ Macedonia
❸ Rumania
❹ Bulgaria
❺ Albania
❻ Greece

This exclusionism is attributable to the survival instincts of peninsular people, i.e., their desire to preserve their racial lineage.

No to foreign races

To mix = to die

People of peninsular countries lived under the constant siege of foreign invaders,

struggling on a daily basis to survive, doing whatever it takes.

Fight or die!!

Inevitably, their personalities became very extreme.

Why so tough??

I need to survive!

With knives constantly at their throats, they had no time for diplomacy or compromise.

Let's resolve this through dialogue.

Only by winning can we live. What dialogue?

Win! Win! Win!

There was no choice but to be stubborn.

I'm always right! We have no other choice here!

Thus, people of peninsular countries tend to be stubborn.

Why are you so stubborn?

Because compromise means death!

Naturally, peninsular people came to possess different personalities compared to those folks living on the continental mainland and islands.

The Chinese — They emphasized unity to ensure peace and security.

Big land does not move far.

No worries!

The Japanese — They emphasized *wa* and avoided conflict to ensure peace and harmony.

What about the Koreans, who were victims of constant foreign invasions?

Advance Attack! Hurrah

The Koreans emphasized as their top priority the protection of their lives and possessions.

My stuff

The method by which the Koreans pursued this may be succinctly expressed by one Chinese character, read as 'choong' in Korean.

*

* Choong

The Koreans use the word *choong* as a prefix or suffix to other Chinese characters to make up words such as faithfulness and loyalty.

But the '*choong*' for the purposes of our discussion has an entirely different meaning.

Let's go back to the original meaning of *choong* quoted in the lectures of Confucius.

* Confucius.

In his writings, Confucius says:

和忠必和中
Ji Choong Pil Ji Jung

In short, it means:

To know choong one must know the middle...

But what did he mean by the 'middle*'?

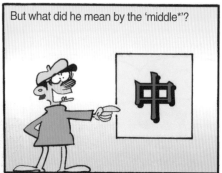

* Pronounced as 'joong' in Korean.

The Chinese character for 'middle' was modeled after the shape of a flag.

In the old days, the Chinese hoisted a flag in the middle of the village.

So, this character, '*joong*,' means middle or center.

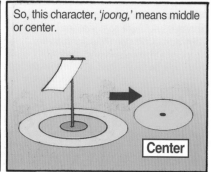

Center

The true meaning of *joong* is 'the great essence of all things,' Confucius said.

中者天下之大本
Joongja Cheonha Ji Daebon.*

* *Joong* is the great essence of all things.

In other words, the spirit of fairness and righteousness that is unfettered by private interests.

This is the mind of *daegongmusa*, i.e., fair, upright and honest disposition.

大公無私*

Fair, upright and honest disposition

* Daegongmusa : Grand rulers do not seek private interests.

The character *choong* resembles the heart (心) embracing *joong*, the center.

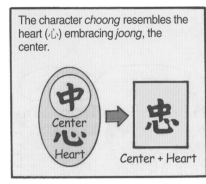

中
Center
心
Heart

➡️

忠

Center + Heart

It is the heart that places common values ahead of personal interests.

Putting my personal feelings aside.

Putting country, society and people ahead!

Another meaning for *joong* is equilibrium.

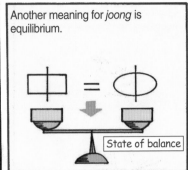

State of balance

In sum, *choong* is a mindset that stresses justice, fairness and sharing.

Choong is the foundation of the Korean scholar's spirit,

which in turn forms the basis of the Korean mentality.

More simply, what is right and fair for all is to be valued,

Values for the good of all

and one must never be fickle because of trivial personal interests!

I'll give you a government job if you do as I say.

No way! I'll keep my honor!

If you understand the essential meaning of *choong*, it will be easier to understand the meaning of commonly used Korean words.

충성(忠誠) (Choong-seong) To be adamantly faithful to one's superior without changing allegiance.

One man cannot serve two masters!

충실(忠實) (Choong-shil) To stubbornly and persistently continue one's work without being fickle.

Nahh... You go ahead. I have to finish my assignment.

Aren't you going home?

충직(忠直) (Choong-jik) To stubbornly uphold uprightness without toleration of deceit.

You are a faithful servant

충신(忠臣) (Choong-shin) A faithful retainer who stubbornly serves his master without changing his allegiance for personal gains.

I shall serve you as long as I live!

Now, if the most important values to Koreans are righteousness and fairness (in the writer's opinion),

忠

Righteous to all people

Fair to all people

what does it really mean to be righteous, and fair to all people?

'Righteous to all people,' of course, doesn't mean 'what is right for only myself.'

It is what all people or society considers as being upright.

This applies to nearly everything-the Korean mentality, attitude and way of life...

Rejecting or attempting to change this is absolutely unacceptable.

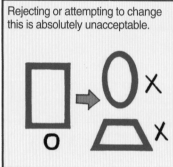

Put another way... you don't want to challenge what society deems to be correct.

This leads to rigid conformance to the values that society believes to be the right values.

In other words, it is a 'yes' or 'no' dichotomy.

For example – 'commies are bad' is a common sentiment shared by the Koreans living on the divided Korean peninsula.

Korean society...

won't accept people praising and accepting communism.

As another example, all Korean people recognize that a harmonious family is a good thing.

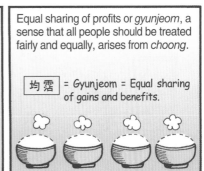

Paradoxically, this is a trait that strikingly resembles socialism.

In a capitalist society, where individual wealth is not equally distributed,

such a trait is bound to disrupt the stability of society.

What kind of behavior does this equal profit mentality spark?

People work like crazy to acquire what others have.

I'm not falling behind!

This did wonders to promote the development of the Korean economy, as you can guess.

Economic growth rate

I did it!

Another important value emphasized by the Koreans is the preservation of the Korean identity.

Korean Identity

The Korean peninsula belongs to one people!

Having survived numerous foreign invasions, the Koreans didn't mix with other races.

I may lose everything but not this!

Pure Bloodline

The preservation of orthodox traditions was a legacy of the *choong* spirit.

Orthodoxy = Foundation of a nation

Legiti-macy

The emphasis on orthodoxy is not only limited to bloodline.

Tradition

Orthodoxy is the emphasis of 'original form.'

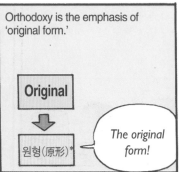

Original

원형(原形)*

The original form!

The original form is what the Koreans recognize as being legitimate and righteous.

Original

This is the original form!

Legitimate!

* Original form

This kind of orthodoxy sticks to original traditions, hardly ever opting for change or revision.

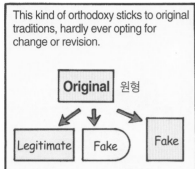

The Koreans guard these cardinal values at all costs.

Over my dead body!!

This is all a result of *choong*.

I shall not go if not the way. I shall not do if not right.

Okay then! As we've seen, the Korean character is well described by this one character, *choong*.

Choong stubbornly preserves values collectively recognized by the community.

I'll keep the promises I made with the people!

Then do it at all costs!

Choong frowns upon fickle people that switch sides very quickly.

How low! Traitor!

Party A

Party B

Two-timing politician!

Choong believes in equal profit sharing.

Choong is exemplified by the extreme, sometimes radical temperament that developed over time

because of the constant foreign invasions.

Rrrrr......!

Choong gave rise to the orthodoxy that rejects changes and distortions in an effort to preserve fundamental beliefs.

Original

Change + Distortion   *No!*

Choong... is the essence of the Korean character.

If I give you my heart...   *It's forever!*

In fact, the many traits represented by *choong* are common traits peculiar to people of peninsular countries.

Stubborn!

Inflexible!

But the clearest manifestation of *choong* has to be the *seonbi* (scholar) spirit of the Koreans.

Seonbi

The *bushi*, Japan's ruling class, lived by a code of ethics known as the *Bushido*.

Bushi

On the other hand, the Korean ruling class armed themselves with the *seonbi* spirit.

We will not commit unjust acts, even if it means losing our lives!

Over time, the *seonbi* spirit formed the spiritual basis of the Korean nation.

Loyalty to country
Devotion to parents
Fraternity
Loyalty to friends

Today, this healthy spirit continues to flow in the soul of the Korean people.

Personal glory is second to Korea's prosperity!

This self-purifying (*jajeong*) spirit acts as a filter to the negative aspects of society...

Seonbi spirit

We're already aware that the *bushi* used to be the ruling class in Japan, right?

Ever since a *bushi* regime known as the Kamakura Bakufu came into power in 1192,

Nobility | Kamakura Bakufu

the *bushi* class ruled Japan for nearly 700 years until the Meiji Restoration occurred in 1868.

Shogun

Leader of the bushi regime

The ruling class needed its own code of ethics.

This code of ethics was the *Bushido* or 'the Way of the Warrior,'

Bushido

which developed in earnest starting from the Kamakura period.

Notice the form of the samurai.

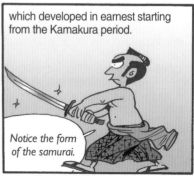

The term *Bushido* started to be used during the Edo period (1603-1867).

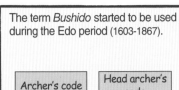

Archer's code	Head archer's code
Soldier's code	Warrior's code

Bushido refers to the special code of ethics of the *bushi* warrior.

Respect honor and fear disgrace.

Such... Such disgrace... The only thing to do...

Train the mind and body for warfare... and build endurance.

husssh

Be faithful to one's master,

Commit suicide!

Yes!

and loyal to one's friend.

Thank you my friend...

Anything for a friend!

Typically, a *bushi* was not afraid to die for honor.

I fight for the honor of the Daira family!

Bushido not only formed the core of the soldier's mind but the spirit of the ruling class during the *Bakufu* period that was controlled by soldiers.

Bushido

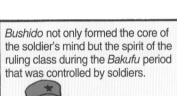

On the contrary, the ruling class of Joseon picked up the pen, living by the *seonbi* code.

Seonbi

What is meant by *seonbi*? Although it occasionally referred to academics who did not hold any government posts...

Confucius says... Mencius says...

generally, people possessing both virtue and knowledge were referred to as *seonbis*.

Seonbinim!

ahem

A man of character, knowledge and virtue...

Seonbi = Man of character

The ruling class of Joseon society had to have this *seonbi* spirit.

That's why the people respect you.

The *seonbi* was expected to be loyal to the country.

A subject can't serve two kings!

King = The state

And kindhearted to the people...

The will of the people is the will of the heavens. I beg you not to turn a blind eye to the people.

He devoted his life to the pursuit of learning.

Etiquette and virtue you say? Just as important as one's life...

The *seonbi* mindset was characterized by impartiality.

I must not harm society just for the sake of my advancement.

The *seonbi* was not to covet unjust enrichment but to be a man of integrity and honesty.

You're trying to bribe me! Take it back!

The *seonbi* was expected to sacrifice his life in order to prevent the occurrence of what he considered to be unjust.

Although I've been sentenced to drink this bowl of poison,

I will not compromise my beliefs!

This *seonbi* spirit prompted the *seonbi* to express his views even with a sword to his throat.

It is unacceptable to delay the reforms!

When the king got off track, the *seonbi* would try to set things straight.

Realize that you have made a grave mistake!

When a national crisis emerged, the *seonbi* took the lead, spearheading the fight against invaders.

The fate of our country... is... like... a candle in the wind... Fight for your fatherland!

The Korean *seonbi* spirit and the Japanese *bushido* were both duties imposed on the ruling class, the equivalent to the concept of *noblesse oblige* in the West.

Noblesse oblige

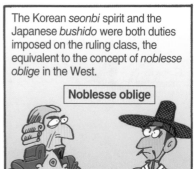

Fair to say the *choong* mentality was at the heart of the *seonbi* spirit.

Seonbi spirit

Here's a list of virtues which members of Korean society were to abide by:

Choong Filial piety Benevolence Faithfulness

Righteousness

The preservation of archetypes also led to the strict adherence to these virtues.

Need to be practical instead of sticking to archetypes!

It may be impractical at times but preserving our roots and our origins is more important!

Me practical   Me original

Thus, a person, regardless of the degree of his success, was branded as an immoral person if he lacked these key virtues.

He accepted a bribe!

How can he call himself a seonbi?

People respected a man possessing a sound *seonbi* spirit regardless of his wealth.

He's a profoundly educated man!

A respectable man indeed.

Today, things haven't changed. People follow and respect upright, straight-shooting and impartial leaders.

A man like him is hard to find these days.

As long as each Korean aspires to live by this *seonbi* spirit,

If all else fails, we must, at least, have the right mentality.

Sure! To avoid becoming fools in front of our kids...

Korea can overcome any obstacle confronting the country.

선비 정신*

* Seonbi spirit

Present and future obstacles included.

This *seonbi* spirit is the force that serves as the gatekeeper to the spirit of modern day Koreans.

Korean Spirit

Seonbi 선비   Spirit 정신

The *seonbi* sprit is very rigid, as what is deemed to be rightful hardly ever changes.

Our decision is absolutely, unequivocally right!

If we're not careful here, our egos won't fit through the door!

This is the *choong* mentality at work...

The Koreans need an upgraded, modern seonbi spirit for the 21st century!

55

As we discussed, due to their different geographical locations,

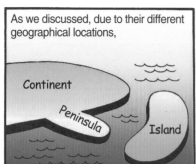

the Chinese, Koreans and Japanese came to possess very different characteristics.

The differences among continental countries, peninsular countries and island countries apply not only to Asian countries, but also to other countries around the world. Shall we take a look?

Analogy time. If China is the representative continental country in Asia, its counterpart in Europe would be France.

These two countries absorbed various races through a policy of toleration and inclusion.

In Chinese, we say 'Da Tong Zhu Yi'!*

Yes! Tolerance! Conciliation and compromise!

* In Korean, Daedongjueui

Both countries also absorbed various cultures and made it into their own.

French culture.

Han culture.

They are both very proud people.

We're the greatest!

When describing France, the French enjoy using words like 'great' or 'grand.'

La grande nation! (Our great nation!)

This is how we refer to our country.

'La grande armee' refers to the French armed forces.

Where did this pride come from? You could say it arises from the illustrious history and culture of each country.

China is the origin of all Asian culture!

We're the father of all European countries. Look at our history!

At the same time, the people of both countries are very individualistic.

It doesn't really matter who the leader is...

That's right. As long as I'm happy...

They refuse to sacrifice themselves for whatever cause.

Huh? Why me?

Yikes! You're crazy!

Now we can also see many similarities between island countries, e.g., Japan and England.

The people of these two countries suffer in various degrees from xenophobia.

I hold my tongue as an English gentleman but that chap is...

Their cultures developed at a slower pace compared to continental countries.

It's not like culture disseminates from the islands!

They had no choice but to accept the cultures of other people.

Island countries have no choice but to accept foreign cultures.

Foreign cultures

But they did so only on a selective basis.

良いとこ取り *

But we accept only what we need!

Foreign cultures were modified to fit their own purposes.

Catholic Church from the continent→ Anglican Church

Anglican Church

* Yoidokotori

The greatest threat they faced was internal strife.

I shouldn't be doing this...

So they avoided conflict.

No contact! *No trouble!*

We do not say (tatemae) what we really feel (honne)... *Roundabout way of expression... Black humor*

The Japanese don't shake hands. They bow instead.

bump

When the English do a handshake, rarely would you see them doing it firmly and vigorously.

How's it going buddy!

shake

shake

They hold the hand lightly and finish off the handshake without much fanfare.

How do you do?

What are they doing?

The people of both countries are very proud.

This pride is attributable to the characteristic of islanders to deify themselves.

It is a very abstract sense of pride.

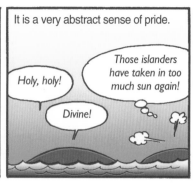

They avoid extreme behavior and language to reduce the chances of confrontation.

They also firmly unite to ward off foreign invaders.

This applies whether a foreign country is invading the state itself or the economy. Red tape is everywhere.

The group comes before the individual. Each person is accountable to the group.

In Japan, it is not rare for a senior manager of a company gone sour to kill himself, hoping society would forgive him.

In times of war, the English nobility rushed to the battlefield, offering their services.

But unthinkable crimes still occur even in Japan where public security is known as being well maintained.

England, in fact, is the home of the infamous hooligans...

Why? Under the stifling conditions of an island, pent up energy is bound to explode in some way.

Meanwhile, the people of the Balkan peninsula exhibit a temperament that is most similar to that of the Koreans.

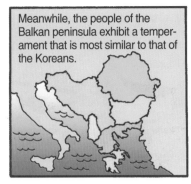

The two people share a common history of suffering for thousands of years from constant foreign invasions.

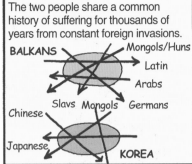

BALKANS
Mongols/Huns
Latin
Arabs
Slavs Mongols Germans
Chinese
Japanese
KOREA

Many different people intermingled on the Balkan peninsula for thousands of years.

Mix of nations
Yugoslavia
Serbia
Turkey
Croatia
Bulgaria
Rumania
Greece
Macedonia
Albania

But, to this day, each people lives in its own country, having preserved its own unique culture.

Rumania
Serbia
Bulgaria
Macedonia
Albania
Greece

Pretty much the same thing the Koreans did to preserve their identity for thousands of years.

The history of my family...

* Family tree

They turned their backs on foreign people in an effort to preserve their racial heritage.

Out-siders not allowed

Of course, this bred enormous pride among such people.

We are a proud people!

They adhered to an orthodoxy that embraced only the fundamental.

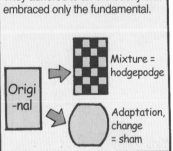

Origi-nal
Mixture = hodgepodge
Adaptation, change = sham

A somewhat drastic and extreme characteristic that developed over a difficult history...

and a very stubborn and uncompromising personality are traits shared by the Koreans and the Balkans.

Coke tastes better!
Uh-uh... Pepsi!!

They did whatever they could do to protect their lives, families and property from foreign invaders.

They're coming again!!

A cooperative spirit and strong group orientation are also similar traits shared by these people.

United we stand, divided we fall!

Eventually, peninsular people learned through history that nobody was going to watch out for themselves.

People came to mistrust others.

My life! My family! My property!

It's me or nothing!

It is a temperament that arose from the special circumstances of peninsular countries.

Kicked this way...

Kicked that way...

It was inevitable that peninsular people developed into a 'tough' people.

Only the strong survive!

These resolute individuals united when necessary,

united defense

but, usually, the word 'compromise' was a foreign language and stubbornness a way of life.

Why don't you do as you're told!

Are you the boss? Why are you telling me what to do?

Characterized by a strong sense of individualism, peninsular people can hardly agree on anything!

This side!

That side!

Over here!

Here!

Most of the Balkan countries are agricultural countries.

There are very few people who migrate.

Balkan peninsula

Each individual unites based on his territorial background and bloodline...

Kosovo!

Albania!

Serbians over here!

But it's a little more complicated in Korea.

Migrating population

Industrialized society

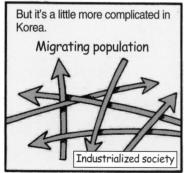

The Koreans instinctively cling to every possible group they can identify with for protection, whether it is based on bloodline, educational background or regional ties.

Educational background

Regional ties

Family ties

Others

Whether it's in Korea or the Balkan peninsula, you'll see that cronyism is alive and well.

M High School, Class of 1988, K Univ., Class of 1992. Born in XX Province, Andong Kim Lineage.

The Korean People

The Korean Character

• Orthodoxy, egalitarianism and cronyism

Been around the world a bit,	so let's identify a few things that can be found only in Korea.	By doing so, we will be able to shed light on some key aspects of the Korean character.

● **First of all, the endless rows of apartment buildings!**

Hong Kong is known to be packed with apartments, but Hong Kong is just a city. There is no other country in the world like Korea that is covered with sprawling apartment complexes throughout the country, whether it is in a metropolitan area or a rural area.

Incredible! Simply incredible!

© The Chosun Ilbo

Think about this. With limited space, if everybody wanted to live in a warm cozy home... What would it take?

Nothing worse than a man without a home!

Moving Center 555-5555

Although you can't smell fresh soil, apartments would be the only alternative.

But no other place in the world has apartment complexes spread across the country like wallpaper.

People live in apartments with the same size, design and layout shared by their neighbors.

Given that the Koreans cannot stand falling behind others,

Does she think wrapping that dead animal around her neck makes her special?

anything different immediately catches the eyes of neighbors.

Oh boy! They're getting a wide-screen TV!

大型TV
42"
PROJECTION TV

Rumors of the new television would then fly all over the apartment complex.

Did you see that new 42-inch wide screen TV?

It's going to be unbearable to see them showing off!

Rumors, words spread like a plague.

Our TV's in perfect condition. Why do you want to buy a new one?

What if your son feels inferior to the next-door neighbor's kid?

Fierce competition ensues...

We're going to get a 42-inch TV!

How about a 53-inch TV!

Umm.. I think 60-inch is the biggest you can buy!

Introduced to the market only a few years ago, refrigerators built for *kimchi* are outselling standard refrigerators.

Kimchi fridge

Standard fridge

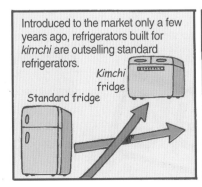

People send their kids to all kinds of after-school tutoring programs to keep them ahead of the pack.

English lesson

Piano lesson

School subject lesson

Art lesson

Computer lesson

The Koreans have taken their 'equal profit sharing' mentality to a whole new level, which, in this modern day, has taken on a new name... 'Apartment disease.'

The kid next door goes to tutors after school.

We can't let our child just sit at home and play!

● Walking through the streets of Korea resembles walking through a labrynth of endless signs. In fiercely competitive Korean society, signs play a crucial role, alerting customers to the location and nature of businesses. Korean signs fight for every inch, having been plastered chaotically on buildings, overlapping in some cases and always looking for the upper hand. A competitive spirit that knows no limit – it's the Korean mentality at work. One must never lose out to a neighbor. This compulsion disfigures the city. Signs on windows... Signs on building walls... Signs posted on rooftops... The signs have taken over.

This sign warfare is also waged by pharmacies that exist to preserve the health of the people.

A pharmacy must make a patient at ease...

Lately, the trend in Korea has been to put up huge signs with bold red letters.

I'm blinded!

* Victory Pharmacy

It's the basic Korean mentality at work: I may not be able to win,

but at least I will not fall behind!

I'm not going to be last!

Me, neither!

Me, neither!

If business owners would just compromise a little, they could display elegant and easy-to-read signs for their customers.

Norebang*
3F
Taekwondo
3F
Pediatrician
2F
Physician
2F
Optician 1F

* Singing room

But this isn't quite that easy for the Koreans, as they engage in a sign warfare, battling as if their lives depend on it.

* Restaurant

● Churches with steeples and red neon crosses...

Nowhere in the world other than in Korea would you find as many churches with steeples! As if there's an unspoken agreement, churches occupying space in commercial buildings maintain steeples on slab roofs. One steeple alone is strange enough to a foreigner, but imagine the sight of three or four steeples on the same rooftop!

Oh, My God!

At night, Seoul transforms into a forest of red neon crosses.

Tourists coming to Korea for the first time are befuddled.

In fact, one might even ask:

Is the entire city of Seoul a graveyard?

Why are there so many red crosses!

Christianity forbids the worshipping of idols...

Thou shall not worship idols!

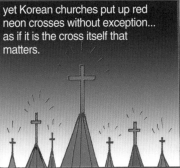

yet Korean churches put up red neon crosses without exception... as if it is the cross itself that matters.

This is another prime example of the Korean temperament.

What others do...

I must do, too!

● The extreme nature of student and labor movements.

Although the situation has markedly improved in recent years, whenever demonstrations or strikes break out, the situation often resembles a war zone. Until the 1970s, Japan also faced violent demonstrations in which spears, gas masks, helmets and shields were commonly utilized. Such demonstrations have largely vanished in Japan. In Korea, however, it is not uncommon to still see rocks and Molotov cocktails flying and steel pipes and wooden clubs being wielded in demonstrations.

© The Chosun Ilbo

Whenever there's a demonstration, there's always someone shaving off all of his or her hair.

The demonstrators commonly tie red bandanas around their heads and raise their fists in the air, as if there's no tomorrow.

They break out the drums and gongs...

They follow the head 'cheerleader' in movements even synchronized swimmers would envy.

Like seasoned professionals, they sing songs, dance and shout slogans in unison.

Foreigners drop their jaws at this sight that can be witnessed only in Korea.

● Nearly 75% of the population is on the go during the Lunar New Year and Chusok (Thanksgiving) holidays.
Among the 46 million Korean population, 32 million people return to their hometowns during these holidays.
Korea is the only country in the world where as many as 75% of the population hit the roads at the same time.

During the holidays, we return to our hometown and visit grandma and grandpa!

Special transportation services are put into place during these holidays, and

The government runs extra trains,

chartered buses and even army vehicles!

24-hour live broadcasts of road and traffic conditions are made available.

Yes... Slow traffic at the Singal Interchange.

Let's keep the roads clean... Refrain from littering...

The Road Home Live Broadcast

Korea's probably the only country in the world that places temporary toilets along the congested parts of the highways.

Men   Wo-men

Of course, many Americans and Europeans also travel during the Christmas and Easter season.

But not all of them travel to spend their entire vacation time visiting parents and relatives....

Gonna catch up on sleep this vacation.

Instead, many people spend vacations at home, resting and relaxing.

Silent night, holy night...

And... many people live in their home-towns, making it unnecessary for them to go very far during the holidays.

My parents, in-laws and friends all live in this town!

There's no need for the great exodus that happens in Korea.

To each region of Korea

1/2 of all Koreans reside in the Seoul metropolitan area

Just like the Koreans, the Chinese are also on the move during the holiday seasons.

Hey... We also consider family to be very important!

But it's a little different in China. Since the country's enormous, going home for many of those who have moved far away is impossible.

I'm broke! And home is so far away!

Another point to consider – industrialization came to China a little late... so many of the people still live as farmers in their hometowns.

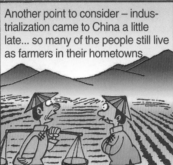

Now, in the case of Taiwan, many people leave for the holiday season, especially for the Lunar New Year holidays.

honk honk

hooonk

But only about half of the 20 million Taiwanese population leave for home.

Going home!   *Can't go!*

50%

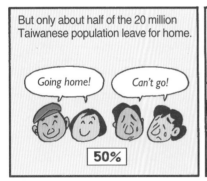

As mentioned above, in Korea, three-quarters of the entire population are on the move during the New Year and Thanksgiving holidays.

Population 46 million people! 32 million hit the roads!

Why do so many Koreans visit their home-towns during the holiday seasons? It's a concept embedded and ingrained in their thoughts.

During the holidays, we must visit our parents. That's the right thing to do...

Because it's the 'right thing' to do, the Koreans are serious about doing it.

Everything else can wait!

I must get the train tickets!!

There are no exceptions.

Why do you have to go to your hometown for Thanksgiving?

Ehhh? Have you lost your mind?

Evidently, this is another manifestation of the *choong* mentality!

Visiting parents during the holiday seasons is the right thing to do as human beings.

Very disrespectful not to!

What are some other unique Korean characteristics? When something catches on, you'll soon see a whole bunch of it spreading like wild fire.

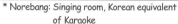

* Norebang: Singing room, Korean equivalent of Karaoke

It's a trait foreigners have a hard time understanding.

Karaoke first made its appearance in Japan during the 1980s,

and its fever soon swept across Japan.

The *Norebang* was introduced to Korea in the 1990s.

Within three years, tens of thousands of *norebangs* sprouted all over Korea. The rate of penetration was far greater than in Japan.

Sweet dreams are made of this... Who am I to disagree...

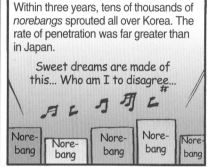

Within two to three years, tens of thousands of Internet cafés called PC *bang* or PC room, a recent phenomenon, opened all over Korea.

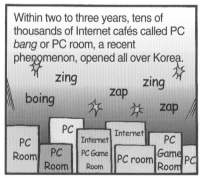

And what about teenagers dyeing their hair?

Japanese teenagers started dyeing their hairs in the early 1970s.

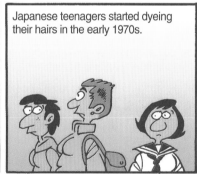

Even when this was a popular new look, there were more Japanese teenagers who did not dye their hair.

As late as in the mid 1990s, Korean people thought it was very strange for youths to dye their hair.

What have you done to your hair? You're not a Westerner, you know!

However, today, teenagers who haven't dyed their hair seem to be the minority.

Oh yes! There's something else you can find only in Korea.

There's a large number of restaurants that stress they're the original thing, or *wonjo*.

Original food for royalty

Authentic Korean food, authentic Japanese food and authentic Chinese food.

Authen-tic	Masan Steamed Fish
Authen-tic	Japanese Food
Authen-tic	Chinese Cuisine

Doesn't stop there. Authentic French, authentic Italian, authentic royal court cuisine...

Authentic French Cuisine La Seine	Authentic Italian Food Toscana	Authentic Korean Food Arirang

They claim their restaurants are where it all started.

Original Jumuleok*
Seoul Restaurant

#1 Jumuleok
Chunghae

Original Jumuleok
Jongno Restaurant

- - - - - -

* Pork or beef barbecued with seasoning

Each restaurant claims to be the original.

Other places are copycats!

Look who's talking!

Original Haejang-guk*

Home of the Haejang-guk

* Soup commonly consumed to relieve hangovers

What does it mean to be 'authentic'?

This is sliced radish kimchi made with our great grandmother's recipe from the Joseon period!

Nothing must have been added or changed.

We've made it with grandma's secret recipe!

In other words, the original purity must not have been impaired.

We make our solleongtang* like they did during the Joseon period!

Original seasonings only without any additives!

* Ox-bone soup

Restaurateurs stress they're the original – not some copycat, outsider that has jumped into the game late.

We're the original. Everybody else is a copycat!

Hey! It's not like you're the only one who makes that!

The fact that the Koreans value authenticity and legitimacy is also exemplified by their attitude towards genealogy.

Family Tree

Sure, there are foreigners who are also keenly interested in genealogy.

Was bestowed the title Earl of Nottingham by Henry VII.

FAMILY CHRONO-

But in Europe, people tend to bring up the family tree to be pretentious.

As you can see... Uhhum... We are of noble lineage!

Otherwise, in general, most people are unaware of their genealogies.

So, tell me about your family line...

What? Am I a dog you want to breed or something??

In Japan, the Japanese were forbidden to have surnames

Don't even dream about having a surname!!

That's saved for nobles and the samurai!

until the Meiji Restoration in 1868.

There are millions of people in the country with the same names. Distinguish them by giving them surnames.

List of Names

Hence, in most cases, except for the nobility,

I'm Fujiwara.

I'm Daira.

most people aren't concerned about their family lines or genealogies.

We have a genealogical table.

He must come from noble or samurai blood.

It's a completely different case in Korea, where families treasure their books of genealogies like family heirlooms.

Fire!

Save the book of genealogy!

The older members of the families periodically update the missing members of the family tree.

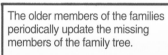

Family Tree of the Hansan Lee Clan

People without genealogical lines are considered 'rootless' families.

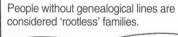

We're financially poor, but

we can't accept a son-in-law with no recorded family line!

Look how rigorously people even scrutinize the pedigree of dogs!

Is this dog really a purebred? Does it have a book of genealogy?

What're you talking about? You want me to break out his pedigree??

Saying someone is 'without a family line' is the same as hurling curse words at that person.

How dare you... You don't even exist in a family tree.

This exemplifies how important the Koreans consider orthodoxy and legitimacy.

Why don't you adopt a child?

Without knowing the child's background? How on earth...

It is difficult to find another people more attached to the issue of legitimacy than the Koreans.

* Legitimacy

During the 500 years of the Joseon Dynasty, there was constant struggle over who was to be the legitimate heir to the throne.

The Joseon Dynasty court, which embraced Confucianism, made it clear that the first son was to inherit the throne.

But the nature of power always breeds exceptions...

Plots, conspiracies and constant feuding...

A clear justification was required to subvert recognized legitimacy.

'Ordinary' justification was not enough. 'Noble' justification was required.

Success or failure in establishing a new legitimacy depended on whether there was a 'noble' justification.

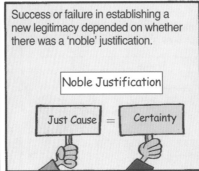

The third king of the Joseon Dynasty, King Taejong, was a fifth son. He resorted to fratricide many times over in order to ascend to the throne.

It was preservation of national security and establishment of authority of the throne.

Among King Taejong's three sons, the third son, who became King Sejong*, was king material.

Tradition dictated that the first son be king.

* King Sejong is considered as one of the greatest rulers in Korean history.

But Prince Chungnyeong's accession to the throne was legitimized by the abdication of his two elder brothers.

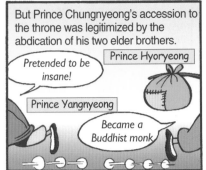

Pretended to be insane!

Prince Hyoryeong

Prince Yangnyeong

Became a Buddhist monk.

The struggle for the throne was fierce throughout the Joseon period.

Being the eldest legitimate son of the king...

and the queen, young prince, you are the lawful successor to the throne.

Power struggles ensued between those in line to inherit the throne and the power figures inside the palace.

For the good of the kingdom···

the most qualified prince, you Boksung, must inherit the throne.

Although the Japanese court also stressed tradition, the most qualified person usually ascended to the throne.

Meritocracy!

The most qualified person will rule!

The emphasis on legitimacy during the Joseon period is well exemplified by the cold treatment people bestowed on illegitimate sons.

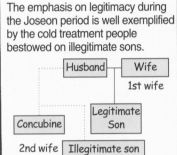

Husband	—	Wife
		1st wife
		Legitimate Son
Concubine		
2nd wife	Illegitimate son	

It didn't matter if one was born into the noblest of families it he was the son of a concubine.

How cursed you are my son! Born into this world as an illegitimate child!

He was never treated as a son nor could he ever hold any government posts.

An illegitimate son can't take the high exam.

Sigh

He was discriminated against in the cruelest ways, forbidden to even utter the word 'father.'

Father...

Eh! The son of a concubine dares to call me father! Shoo!

The first novel written using the Korean alphabet, *Hangeul*, was 'Hong Gil-dong Jeon.'*

My lord, Gildong at your service.

Poor child... Can't even call him father...

* The Life of Hong, Gil-dong

This novel portrays the hardship and pain of an illegitimate child...

I shall put an end to this kind of discrimination with my own hands!

Remnants of this need for legitimacy and orthodoxy can still be found in Korea.

Is he the son of a first wife?

Or a second wife?

Although society has made many strides since then, you can still see hints of the past showing their faces.

What men have concubines these days?

Just asking... You never know...

The Koreans like to insist on being legit and to stick to the original plan of things.

They dislike things that stray from the original...

This is a product of the exclusionary behavior of people trying to hold on to their special privileges...

No longer existing now, there used to be a number of prestigious high schools that everyone aspired to attend.

People considered passing the difficult entrance exam as the 'legitimate' way of entering these schools...

These so-called authentic students bullied and alienated transfer students and those filling vacancies.

When the government abolished the entrance exam and switched to a lottery system,

the former students who had taken the entrance exam didn't acknowledge the 'lottery' students as fellow alumni.

Same thing happens in the work place.

Infatuation with the original...
Reluctance to accommodate change...

These characteristics, of course, are also evident in Korean culture.

$$\text{Original} = \text{Tradition} + \text{Legitimacy}$$

The Japanese way of thinking, however, is very different.

Japan's an island

Tell me something I didn't know...

As an island country, Japan had no choice but to accept things foreign, whether it was culture or goods...

Listen to me. We have to accept foreign cultures and goods. There's no point in stressing legitimacy and origin!

Why? Someone else invented it anyway!

Island country

Foreign countries

Rather than preserving the original shape of an import, the Japanese modified it to fit their particular needs.

Compared to the Koreans that stuck, without exception, to the original, whether native or foreign,

Original recipe!

the Japanese modified what belonged to others, making it suitable for themselves.

Application!

The Japanese leave a lot of room for change, making practical revisions to suit their needs.

Supplement

Change

Supplement

Change

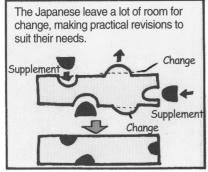

The different mentalities are also exemplified by the way the Koreans and the Japanese read Chinese characters.

Chinese Characters

Chinese characters are used in both Korea and Japan.

Chinese characters

The Japanese have different ways of reading the same Chinese character.

Reading Chinese characters the Japanese way is practically impossible for a foreigner!

There are two ways of reading Chinese characters in Japan. One way is the phonetic approach, *Onyomi*, the phonetic reading of the Chinese characters.

Kuruma

Sha

Hikoki

Shinkansen

And the other way is the semantic approach, *Kunyomi*, the semantic reading of the Chinese characters.

男	犬	竹
Otoko (Man)	Inu (Dog)	Take (Bamboo tree)
酒	組	朝
Sake (Wine)	Kumi (Gathering)	Asa (Morning)

It's confusing when the Japanese switch back and forth between the two pronunciation methods to suit their needs.

Phonetic reading + Semantic reading

What makes matter worse, they also have different ways of pronouncing the same word.

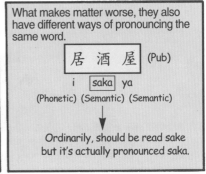

居 酒 屋 (Pub)

i　saka　ya

(Phonetic) (Semantic) (Semantic)

↓

Ordinarily, should be read sake but it's actually pronounced saka.

There are plenty of examples where *Onyomi* and *Kunyomi* are mixed.

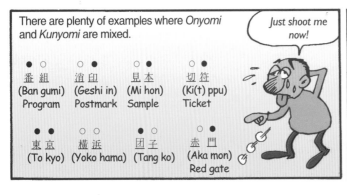

● ○	○ ●	○ ●	○ ●
番 組	消 印	見 本	切 符
(Ban gumi)	(Geshi in)	(Mi hon)	(Ki(t) ppu)
Program	Postmark	Sample	Ticket

● ●	○ ○	● ○	○ ●
東 京	横 浜	団 子	赤 門
(To kyo)	(Yoko hama)	(Tang ko)	(Aka mon) Red gate

Just shoot me now!

From time to time, even the Japanese themselves get confused.

How do you read this?

Geez... I'm not sure either!

Mixing and interchanging the phonetic and semantic readings—this is a very difficult task for foreigners trying to learn Japanese and its Chinese characters.

That's hunseng?

No... It's sinagawa.

品川

The Chinese are also sticklers for traditions.

Chinese culture's the legitimate East Asian culture!

However, China was plagued by countless wars throughout its history.

argg　waag

Existing dynasties were overthrown on many occasions.

Face reality, buddy!

The Chinese people had to recognize their predicament and side with power instead of legitimacy.

We had no choice but to revolt! It was for the people!

They all say the same thing... But what can a guy do? That's life...

With good reason and a proper justification...

I'm taking over! The king's much too ugly!

That's not a proper justification!

the overthrowing of a dynasty was accepted.

So when the new ruffian stormed the palace and became king, the name on the mailbox changed, of course...

I'm starting my own dynasty! Out!

In Korea, Yi Seong-gye staged a coup d'etat and overthrew the Wang family that ruled Goryo to establish Joseon.

Wang Dynasty

Yi Dynasty

The Chinese sided with practicality instead of stubbornly adhering to orthodoxy.

Reality

Orthodoxy

Things change anyway...

The Chinese even greatly simplified their own Chinese characters...

It's too hard to write!

Takes too long and it's a hassle!

More than 2,200 Chinese characters have been simplified.

Simplified Characters (簡體)

1951. 1. Chinese government enacts draft plan to simplify Chinese characters
1956. Chinese character simplification plan promulgated
1986. Amended simplification plan promulgated

2,235 characters

Examples of Simplified Chinese Characters

① Alteration of archaic letters	② Reduction or elimination of parts	③ Preservation of only certain parts	④ Change of complicated parts to symbols	⑤ Creation of new characters
气 ← 氣	标 ← 標	声 ← 聲	戏 ← 戲	毕 ← 畢
从 ← 從	竞 ← 競	厂 ← 廠	鸡 ← 鷄	华 ← 華
车 ← 車	单 ← 單	习 ← 習	汉 ← 漢	尘 ← 塵
万 ← 萬	冲 ← 沖	乡 ← 鄉	岁 ← 歲	宝 ← 寶

This wasn't accepted by the Koreans, who, of course, emphasize legitimacy and orthodoxy.

What! Change the original thing because it's difficult?

As a result, the Koreans still use the original Chinese characters...

The simplified characters have nothing to do with us!

ORIGINAL

We'd be breaking a tradition of thousands of years if we change the form of Chinese characters.

TRADITION

Unlike Japanese, the Korean language does not have a semantic method of reading Chinese characters.

Haneul* X

Cheon O*

天
Heaven

* Korean word for the 'heavens'
* Phonetic reading of the Chinese character for the 'heavens'

There is only one way of reading Chinese characters—pronouncing the sound of each character precisely.

Earth ji
Yellow hwang
Heaven cheon
Dark hyun

There are only a few exceptions to this rule.

Exceptions

金 pronounced 'Gim' or 'Geum'
金永秀 Gim Yeong-su (person's name)
金剛山 Geumgang-san (Mt. Geumgang)

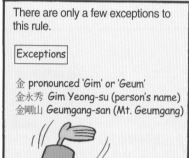

If these few exceptions are kept in mind, there shouldn't be problems reading Chinese characters in conjunction with Korean.

Memorize these few exceptions to the rule.

樂山樂水＝nak-san-nak-su X
　　　　 yo-san-yo-su O
內人＝nae-in X
　　 na-in O

70% of the Korean language is derived from Chinese words but only one pronunciation is recognized for each character.

Je-gong?

In Korean that could mean... 'offer' 'offerings' 'mastery of the air,' 'gentleman,' etc.

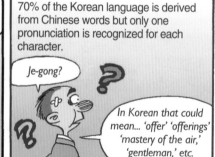

A homonym, when spoken or written only in the Korean alphabet, may at times be confusing because the equivalent Chinese character meaning would be different depending on the context.

정의 ＝ 正義, 定擬, 定議, 定義,
　　　 正意, 正倚, 征衣, 廷議,
　　　 淨衣, 情誼, 情義, 精意

Sometimes, sticking to traditions and the original of things...

Original

causes its fair share of headaches.

Can't break through to the other side!!

Switching topics... they say it's hard to make friends in Korea.

Why? Due to Confucian traditions, it is important to be aware of hierarchy and rank in Korean society.

Age Title   etc., etc.

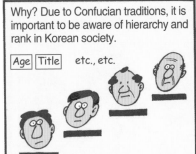

It is easy to became acquainted, but difficult to become bosom buddies, with another person.

What does age have to do with anything? It's everything. A wide gap in age prevents people from becoming friends.

How old are you?? Still wet behind the ears, and you're trying to be an equal?

What about differences in job titles? Chalk it up as another obstacle...

Hey chief... Can we be friends?

Have you completely lost your mind? What do you take me for?

Generational differences are another obstacle...

Sunbae-nim! (Dear senior)

Hubae! (Junior)

In the West, age, status and generation gaps can be transcended in establishing friendships.

Hey Peter!

Hi, Charlie!

However, in Korea, it's difficult to transcend such barriers and form relationships.

You mocking me?

How dare you informally address a seonbae!

Friendships can only be established when various factors are relatively equal...

Similar in age...

Similar titles...

A group of persons can remain as friends as long as they maintain similar titles.

Next round's on me!

Cool!

However, if one of them should move up high in a promotion...

or down in a demotion...

• baekbu (uncle, father's older brother) • sukbu (father's younger brother) • dangjil (male cousin's son) • dongseo (brother-in-law) • jahyeong (older sister's husband) • gomo (aunt, father's sister) • imo (maternal aunt) • dangsuk (father's male cousin) • cheohyeong (sister-in-law) • maehyeong (older sister's husband) • saengjil (nephew) • danggomo (grandfather's niece on the brother's side) • dangsukbu (father's male cousin) • jabu (daughter-in-law) • cheojae (wife's younger sister) • maejae (younger sister's husband) • ijongsachon (cousin by maternal aunt)

First of all, age is taken into account.

Cheol-ho
age 25

Yeong-ho
age 20

The older person can call the younger person by name.

Hey Yeongho!

What's up, hyung*?

* Elder brother

But, the younger person can never call the older person by name. Only by title and degree of kinship...

Cheol-ho!

Are you crazy? Calling your elder brother by his name??

It's especially difficult for women when they marry.

Yeong-ho! It's for you!

Calling her brother-in-law by name! She must be of low descent!

A married woman must always use the appropriate titles when addressing her in-laws.

Doryeonnim!* It's for you!

Thanks hyeongsunim!*

* Husband's younger brother
* Older brother's wife

A wife calls her husband's older brother, *siajubeonim*, or elder brother-in-law.

Siajubeonim* called today.

Yes? What did hyung* say?

* Elder brother-in-law
* Elder brother

A married woman calls her husband's younger brother *doryeonnim** when he's single...

Doryeonnim, time for dinner.

* Husband's younger brother

And when he gets married, she calls him *seobangnim**.

Seobangnim, how's the job going?

Okay, thanks to you, hyeongsunim.

* Husband's younger brother (after he marries)

A wife calls her husband's older sister, *hyeongnim**,

How are you?

Hyeongnim, welcome home.

* Elder sister-in-law

---

and her husband's younger sister, *agassi*.*

Agassi*, have you set a wedding date?

Yes, Eonni*, the 15th of next month.

If a married woman fails to accurately use all these titles for her in-laws, she will be considered uncultured and uneducated.

Yeongja!

How ignorant! Calling her husband's sister by name!

Marriage life would be anything but easy...

How did you end up marrying an uncivilized woman like that?

She doesn't even know basic etiquette?!

* Younger sister-in-law
* Literally, elder sister (in this context, elder brother's wife)

Let's now break down the family relationship. The unit representing the distance between relatives is 'chon.'

Chon = Degree of Kinship

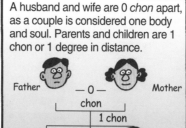

A husband and wife are 0 *chon* apart, as a couple is considered one body and soul. Parents and children are 1 chon or 1 degree in distance.

Father — 0 — Mother
chon
1 chon

What about the relationship between siblings?

Mother — Father
1 chon | 1 chon
Elder son   Younger son

1 chon + 1 chon = 2 chon (siblings)

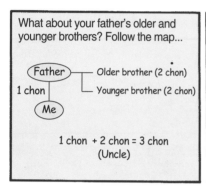

What about your father's older and younger brothers? Follow the map...

Father — Older brother (2 chon)
1 chon └── Younger brother (2 chon)
Me

1 chon + 2 chon = 3 chon
(Uncle)

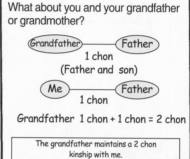

What about you and your grandfather or grandmother?

Grandfather — Father
1 chon
(Father and son)

Me — Father
1 chon

Grandfather 1 chon + 1 chon = 2 chon

The grandfather maintains a 2 chon kinship with me.

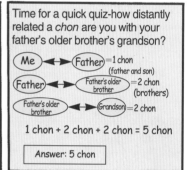

Time for a quick quiz—how distantly related a *chon* are you with your father's older brother's grandson?

Me ⟷ Father = 1 chon (father and son)
Father ⟷ Father's older brother = 2 chon (brothers)
Father's older brother ⟷ Grandson = 2 chon

1 chon + 2 chon + 2 chon = 5 chon

Answer: 5 chon

Now, there are different titles for different levels and degrees of kinship (*chon*) in a Korean family. It may look complicated, but the Koreans must be aware of these titles.

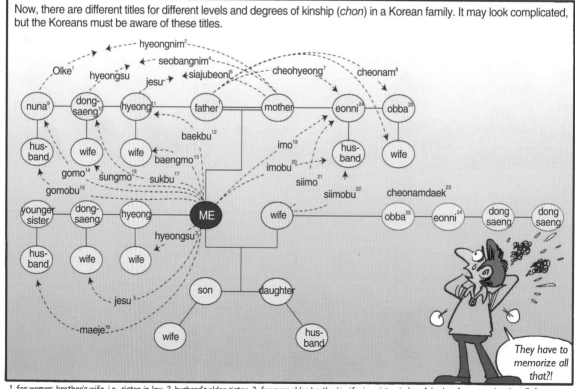

They have to memorize all that?!

1. for women: brother's wife, i.e., sister-in-law 2. husband's older sister 3. for men: older brother's wife, i.e., sister-in-law 4. husband's younger brother 5. for men: younger brother's wife 6. husband's older brother 7. wife's older sister 8. wife's brother, older and younger 9. a man's older sister 10. younger brother(or sister) 11. older brother 12. father's older brother, elder uncle 13. elder aunt 14. aunt on the father's side 15. uncle, aunt's husband 16. aunt, wife of father's younger brother 17. father's younger brother 18. for men: younger sister's husband 19. aunt, mother's sister 20. maternal aunt's husband 21. husband's imo, aunt on the mother's side 22. siimo's husband 23. wife of cheonam, brother-in-law 24. for women: elder sister 25. for women: elder brother

As you can see, Korea's a very hierarchical society.

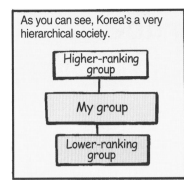

Friendships are only possible between people on level playing fields.

This is the only group to which I can belong.

In order to increase their spheres of influence and power, the Koreans look to expand the scope of the horizontal associations to which they belong.

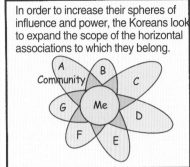

You won't find another country where one person belongs to so many groups.

- Secretary of K High Alumni Association
- Member of XX Association
- Director of XX Research Center
- Chairman of XX Club

For instance, the elementary school alumni associations,

Kids I grew up with! That puts us on equal ground.

middle and high school and university alumni associations,

All graduated from the same schools... Puts us on level ground!

XX High 43rd Graduates' Alumni Association

gatherings of army reserve officers,

We share the common ground of having served as officers in the past!

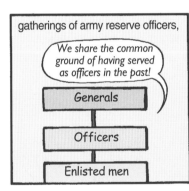

not to mention hometown associations,

Coming from the same hometown, we are on an equal, horizontal level!

and also family clan meetings.

We are in even relationship since we all share the same blood of the XX Lee family.

The XX Clan

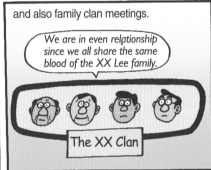

The majority of Koreans are involved in a countless number of groups.

The more the better! My sphere of influence will grow!

In a hierarchical society, this horizontal association is a means of protecting oneself.

All of this exemplifies the deeply rooted cronyism in Korean society.

If abused,

there is a risk that we may become exclusionary collectivists.

The World Record Parade

The Koreans are the most _____ people in the world.

extreme

clever

diligent

unique

aggressive

intense

fiery

"Choose the right answer from the choices given..."

"I see there are both positive and negative connotations..."

Have you found the answer? The answer is...

Ha ha ha! You're all right! All of them are the answer.

clap clap clap clap clap

Some Koreans may get upset but these answers do not necessarily have negative connotations.

You're saying Koreans are extreme, fiery and aggressive?

Although there is no one correct answer, 'extreme' is probably the best word to describe the Korean personality.

Extreme = utmost, ultra, radical, drastic and excessive.

Dictionary

No place in the world would you find a more extreme people. Only in Korea!

Unbelievable!

KOREA

Would it be an exaggeration to say that everything is extreme and drastic in Korea?

What is meant by this?

I can't go any further than this!

Let's look at Korean food as an example.

In the first place, there needs to be a full table.

There's no other people in the world who eat such hot and spicy food!

whoo hooo hooo hooo

How in the world can he eat that?

When it comes to being spicy, Indian food is also said to be very spicy.

It's pretty spicy because of the curry.

Most Indian food contains curry.

whooo

But when ordering at an Indian restaurant, you can choose from various degrees of spiciness.

Give me something that's not spicy, please.

The degree of spiciness is marked with a number of stars next to the dishes.

Some people say Mexican food's spicy, but that's nothing compared to Korean food.

Try some tabasco, which is the Mexican version of Korean gochujang.*

You call this spicy?

* Red pepper paste

Nearly all Korean food is spicy...

ahhhh!

Hot and spicy!

The Koreans need a simmering stew and sizzling food on the table to feel like they've had a complete meal.

Bulgogi*? Galbi*? Samgyeopsal*? Jigae*? Jeongol*?

Do you have only roasted and boiled food?

The food is served hot, so hot that it's easy to burn your tongue and mouth.

Enjoy! Before it gets cold!

How do you expect me to eat something that hot!

* Marinated beef / ribs / Korean-style bacon / stew / Korean-style chowder

The Koreans even sprinkle red pepper powder into an already spicy and simmering stew. And, what do they say after the first spoon?

Ahh... Now that's refreshing...

Spiciness is not just a taste. It's a sensation...

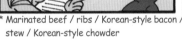

Sweet, bitter, sour, salty

Taste

Spicy

Stimulus Sensation

TASTE

FEELING

So the point is that... the Koreans eat spicy food not for the taste but for the stimulating sensation.

When you get used to spicy food, nothing else quite makes the cut.

* Gochujang (red pepper paste)

85

It wasn't always like this.

Red pepper was introduced to Korea during the Japanese invasions in the late 16th century.

Red Pepper **capsicum annuum**
Originally from South America. The chemical combination $C_{18}H_{27}O_3N$ makes peppers hot. Introduced to Korea from Japan during the 16th-century Hideyoshi invasions.

Since then, for over 300 years, the Koreans have been making it hotter and spicier so that, today, they have the hottest food in the world.

Hot!

Hotter!

Unbearably hot!

In other words, the Koreans have become accustomed to the sensation of extremely hot and spicy food.

Westerners don't eat spicy food.

But we can go look for Western food wherever we go.

스테이크 하우
ステーキ ハウス
STEAK HOUSE

The Koreans have a hard time adjusting to the food when traveling abroad.

American and Japanese food are anything but spicy... Yuck...

Take a look at this bland and greasy food!

So they go on the hunt for Korean restaurants.

Is there a Korean restaurant around here?

What I wouldn't do for a spicy bowl of Yukgyejang* ...mmmm...

K TOUR

* Spicy shredded soup

It's not the craving for Korean food that drives them to Korean restaurants.

Instead of looking for Korean restaurants,

why don't you try some beef stew or other soups?

K TOUR

They're looking for that bang they can only get from hot and spicy food.

Who said we wanted some plain beef stew?

Something hot and simmering would hit the spot! Beef stew...

It's almost a 'withdrawal effect.' Less spicier food won't give them the bang.

Hey, you have any gochujang* left?

I've run out but I got some spicy ramen soup mix.

* Hot pepper paste

Because of the Korean affinity for hot and spicy food, they're number one in the world when it comes to stomach illnesses.

Koreans have the highest rate of intestinal cancer in the world.

How could their intestines survive?

Once you're hooked on the sensation of hot food, there's no turning back.

Oh, yes! It's so good and spicy.

More and more Japanese are beginning to enjoy Korean food... It's that stimulus at work, that rush of eating spicy food...

Karai (spicy!)
Atsui! (hot!)
Oishii! (delicious!)

韓国食堂
ソウル館

bustle
bustle

The Koreans, who take eating spicy food to the extreme,

also take drinking to the extreme.

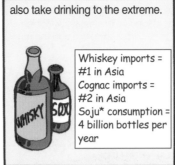

Whiskey imports = #1 in Asia
Cognac imports = #2 in Asia
Soju* consumption = 4 billion bottles per year

* Korean equivalent of vodka

The younger people show some restraint and generally know when to call it a night.

You don't want anymore?

No, I have to work tomorrow.

But many people in the older generations have to go all the way.

Let's call it a night. It's already our fourth bar.

What are you talking about? One more glass! Just one more!

They go from one drinking spot to another getting absolutely tanked.

1st dive → 2nd hole → 3rd cove → 4th spot

They pass around one cup, signifying the 'all for one and one for all' mentality.

Take my glass!

Drink and pass it along!

'If I drink, you have to drink.'
This mentality may be traced to the 'egalitarianism' prevailing in Korean society.

I can't drink! Really...

Everybody else's drinking but you! Take it or die!

There is also a drink called 'poktanju' (poktan = bomb, ju = drink) (known as boilermaker in the West) which is made by dropping a glass full of whiskey into a glass full of beer.

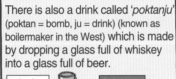

Whiskey

Poktanju

Beer

The poktanju was 'invented' by soldiers who, until recently, governed Korean society.

cheers!

The drink is indeed like a bomb because it levels whoever it comes into contact with!

mommy

Whether it is regarding food or alcohol, the Koreans display this extreme personality.

Take it to the end!

crash!

Doesn't end here... when it comes to swearing. Oh man! Cover your ears!

We're the world champs in swearing.

Shall we look at what some people consider as the most important aspect of society?

Along with the folk religions of Korea, add Christianity, Buddhism, Confucianism and Islam to the mix.

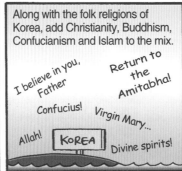

I believe in you, Father

Return to the Amitabha!

Confucius!

Virgin Mary...

Allah!

KOREA

Divine spirits!

Korean Christianity especially has some surprisingly unique elements not found anywhere else in the world today. Not found in the history of the world for that matter.

UNBELIEVABLE!

Korean Christianity

Christianity was introduced to Korea in the form of Catholicism during the 17th century.

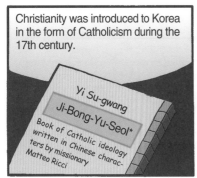

Yi Su-gwang
Ji-Bong-Yu-Seol*
Book of Catholic ideology written in Chinese characters by missionary Matteo Ricci

At the time, when Catholicism entered the country, the Koreans didn't consider it as a religion. They merely considered it as a Western institution.

Westerners think the world is round.

Those ignorant fools.

As Catholicism started to gain a larger following, however, during the 19th century, the government started to suppress it.

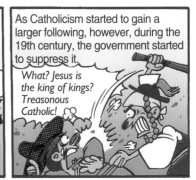

What? Jesus is the king of kings? Treasonous Catholic!

Many churches were formed during the Japanese occupation of Korea(1910-1945). They made significant contributions to Korea's independence movement.

People of Korea must wake up!

Keep knocking at the door and it will open. Till we find our freedom.

But Christianity (Protestantism) spread in earnest throughout Korea...

Believe and attain salvation ('guwon,' in Korean)

What?? Will you give me 9 (=gu) won?

as the U.S. military rolled into town after Korea's liberation from Japan in 1945.

Jesus Christ

Oh, my god!

Merry Christmas!

??

Christianity's explosion happened during the 1970s

Bang

when Korea's economy started to develop at a rapid pace.

Korean Economy

$

Korean Christianity

In other words, it has only been three decades since Christianity has become a mainstream religion in Korea.

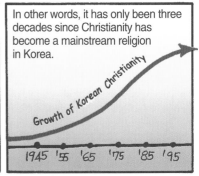

Growth of Korean Christianity

1945 '55 '65 '75 '85 '95

Currently, there're at least 15 million Christians (including Catholics) living in Korea.

It's impossible to get an exact count!

That's nearly 35% of the entire Korean population. Astonishing to say the least.

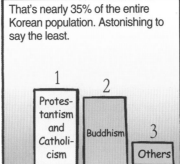

1 Protestantism and Catholicism

2 Buddhism

3 Others

Take a look at these numbers—over 50,000 churches spread across the country and over 10,000 churches in Seoul alone. The most in Asia.

The five largest protestant churches in the world are in Seoul!

That's really a church?

In a span of only 30 years, nearly 35% of the Korean population have become Christians!

That's a world record! Definitely the first time in history that has happened!

I'm surprised, too.

Heaven↗

In the history of humankind, this kind of phenomenon has happened only in Korea.

In Europe, it took several hundreds of years for Christianity to spread.

Wake up! It's the 8th century!

You still believe in those pagan gods?

Christianity crossed over into Japan from Portugal nearly 100 years before it hit the shores of Korea.

However, Christians now make up less than 1% of the Japanese population.

Hey, you observe Christmas?

No, it's just a holiday. There's no religious meaning.

Before Christianity could spread into China, the socialist government declared that religion was a mere opium of the people.

Religion... The opium of the people!

Karl Marx

In Taiwan, it's very difficult to see a church.

Is there a church around here?

I think I saw one around somewhere but... I can't quite remember...

What's the reason for Korea's world-record-breaking growth of Christianity?

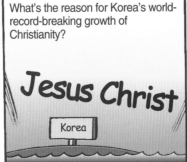

Jesus Christ

Korea

And what's the reason for its lack of appeal in China and Japan?

Iesu Kirisuto?

Japan

Yesu Kristo?

China

China has a countless number of religions.

With a population of 1.3 billion, there're all kinds of religions here.

Religion was suppressed in China after the Communists took over.

No god's going to deliver you! Socialism will!

Most of its religions supplicate for personal and family happiness.

Please let me make a lot of money and stay healthy.

Fortune-Wishing Faith

The huge difference between Christianity in Korea and Japan is attributable to the difference in their religious foundations.

Oh, Abeoji (Father)

Kamisama (Goddess)...

Clap Clap Clap

Japan's native religion is animism...

animism

Originated from the Latin word *anima*
Anima: *Soul, life, to blow in life*
Animal: Living organism
Animation: = Moving picture

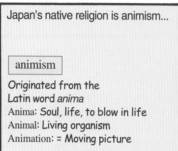

In other words, the Japanese believed that all things in existence have souls.

Soul of the wind

Soul of a tree | Soul of a rock

They believed rocks, trees, grass, animals... all existence for that matter had souls. Hence, all beings are deities.

rock   grass   mountain
river   ocean   forest

Very polytheistic in nature. Needless to say, there're many so-called gods running around in Japan.

bustle bustle

↑ sound of the gods

There are over 8 million 'gods' in Japan because of its religious roots being grounded in animism.

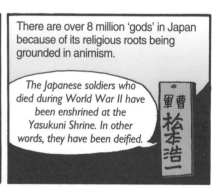

The Japanese soldiers who died during World War II have been enshrined at the Yasukuni Shrine. In other words, they have been deified.

軍曹 松本浩一

Thus, polytheism, which is rooted in animism, is the foundation of all Japanese religions.

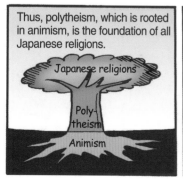

Japanese religions

Poly-theism

Animism

To make a long story short, this all boiled down to Shintoism, with Amaterasu-O-mi-kami as the founding goddess.

Shintoism has become Japan's basic religion.

Animism   Polytheism

Influence of Buddhism

Japanese gods

Japanese legends

Amaterasu-O-mi-kami → Shintoism

Monotheistic religions didn't stand a chance in Japan.

There's only one God.

Nonsense!

Meanwhile, the native religions of Korea started from shamanism. It's the opposite from Japan.

Shamanism

Shamanism started among the natives living in northern Siberia and spread across the Far East, to places like Mongolia and the Korean peninsula.

It's a mysterious and vast world...

Whenever spring comes, the flowers bloom and plants start to sprout...

Contrary to animism that believed everything had souls...

All these events are the doings of some invisible, omnipotent, omniscient and spiritual being...

An absolute being! Some kind of divinity exists! I'm sure of it...

Thunder

Shamans made contact with this god, as well as the spirits of the dead.

Your average Joe from the streets can't meet such a divine existence.

Only a few select, sacred and holy people can meet such a god.

They called the spirits from the dead and prophesied about the future, good or bad.

O' divine one! Let our harvest be bountiful this year!

Let misfortune fall far away from this village!

The shamans were in constant contact with these divine and dead spirits...

Umm... I have a license to do business with the spirits!

rattle rattle

My name... 'mudang' (Shaman)...

In short, the shamanism belief was that there is only one supreme being governing nature.

Animism | Shamanism

All beings come with souls

One great divine being

That's totally ridiculous!

Although rudimentary in nature, shamanism and the monotheistic ideology have a lot in common.

Shamanism → Monotheistic ideology

Mixed Bag of Gods

This is why the Koreans could be so receptive to Christianity.

There's only one omnipotent and omniscient God!

That's right! Heard that before!

Compared to Japan, which was a fundamental Buddhist country up until the Meiji Restoration in 1868,

Buddha says not to kill animals...

Don't eat meat, only fish!

Korea was a Confucian country, which had a lot to do with the explosive growth of Christianity.

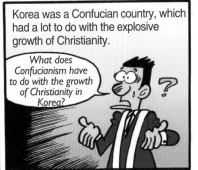

What does Confucianism have to do with the growth of Christianity in Korea?

Well, just how extreme are the ideologies of the Koreans?

The first socialist country was born after the Bolshevik Revolution in 1917.

For over 70 years, ideological conflicts plagued the world.

Capitalism and communism are the opposites of each other... like water and vinegar.

Korean capitalism is...

the most extreme form of capitalism, exemplified by the chaebol!

* Conglomerates

What about North Korea?

Although nearly all the communist countries have fallen, the North Koreans still cling to the most extreme form of Stalinism...

Devotion!

Won't change even if I die!

No way! Never going to convert!

In the name of Stalinism, dissenters in North Korea are quelled by force.

Oops...

A secret police force keeps the people under constant surveillance.

One all-powerful dictator acts like an emperor.

Allegiance!

Long live the Great Leader!

North Korea is a totalitarian state, an egregiously undemocratic and dictatorial nation.

Refusing to obey the Dear Leader's orders

is an act of treason against the party.

Unconditional obedience

North Korea has cut all ties with the West.

After the division of Korea, North Korea stubbornly adhered to a policy of self-reliance... becoming the most isolated country in the world.

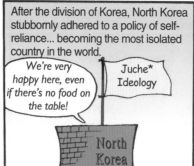

* Self-reliance

Kim Il Sung became the ruler of North Korea in 1945.

He ruled North Korea for nearly 50 years until his death in 1994.

He is recorded in history as a dictator who stayed in power longer than any other dictator in history.

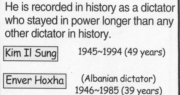

Kim Il Sung	1945~1994 (49 years)
Enver Hoxha	(Albanian dictator) 1946~1985 (39 years)
Nicolae Ceausescu	(Rumanian dictator) 1960~1989 (29 years)
Joseph Stalin	(Soviet Union) 1924~1953 (29 years)

In other socialist countries, when a dictator dies or is ousted from power,

he usually becomes the subject of bitter criticism.

Let's look at Stalin who ruled the Soviet Union with an iron hand for 30 years...

Soon after Stalin's death, his successor Nikita Khrushchev denounced Stalin as a 'dictator.' Stalin was posthumously stripped of all of his honor.

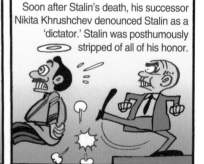

Look at Mao Zedong (1893-1976), the leader of China's communist revolution.

After his death, his wife Jiang Qing was convicted and executed as being one of the four ringleaders of the Cultural Revolution.

However, things have been different in North Korea. Even after Kim Il Sung's death, the people continue to worship him, as if he were a god.

His words and achievements and even his place of birth are all revered to this day.

This is where the great leader

Kim Il Sung fought as a guerilla and ousted the Japanese!

But what was the landmark event of the 20th century among socialist countries?

North Korea's 'Great Leader,' Kim Il Sung, handed over power to his son Kim Jong Il,

Power

a phenomenon that was only possible in a monarchy (which, after all, the Communists overthrew in Russia).

But most monarchies do not hold real power. This happened in a country that is supposed to be 'democratic.'

Why do they call themselves a democracy?

Even other socialist countries were appalled...

How can something like that happen in a socialist country?

Come on! Those North Koreans are eccentric!

* North Korea's officially known as 'The Democratic People's Republic of Korea'

What did the Rumanian dictator Ceausescu think of North Korea?

I envy them so much!

He tried imitating North Korea by handing over power to his son.

Let's look to the North Koreans as a benchmark!

Like the North Koreans, I'm going to hand over power to my son.

1st in power: Me
2nd in power: My wife
3rd in power: My eldest son

key government posts: younger son, son-in-law, daughter, other relatives

However, things didn't work out quite that smoothly. A revolutionary army overthrew him on December 25, 1989.

Revolution!

They riddled the dictator and his wife with hundreds of bullets.

ehhhhh

That's enough!

ooooouch

North Korea has acomplished what others could not even dream about.

If you want to do it, go all the way like we did... Don't be wimps..

How extreme are the North Koreans to have the only modern day, monarchal socialist country!

Monarchal Socialism

Whew... Only possible in North Korea...

95

On the other side of the border, the South Koreans followed the road towards democracy.

Capitalism in Korea also went to the farthest of extremes... typical for Koreans.

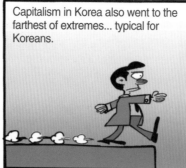

It is a country where one person owns and controls huge conglomerate groups,

for which he makes all the decisions, acting very much like an emperor in his own right.

Do it!

Yes sir!

The top 10 conglomerates in Korea are all chaebols. Korea's a conglomerate-based capitalistic country.

Samsung Group	Chaebol
LG Group	Chaebol
Hyundai Group	Chaebol
	Chaebol

You can find many cases in capitalist countries where one family runs a company... or two...

It's a family business.

It's rare, however, to find the largest conglomerates controlled by a few families...

From ramen noodles to missiles! We make them all!

Chaebol Republic

In these conglomerates, the chaebol owner passes down management powers to his son.

I hand this over to you. You run it!

Management

Passing ownership control of a conglomerate group of companies to one's children, grand children and so forth is something unthinkable in other countries.

The CEO's elected at the shareholders' meeting.

Shareholders' Meeting

Thus, the Korean economy is characterized by an unusual 'patrimonial chaebol capitalism system.'

Only possible in Korea.

Patrimonial Chaebol Capitalism

The owner of a conglomerate is no different than an emperor.

Whether management powers over large conglomerates are passed on to one's son,

or whether control of the state is

passed on to one's son,

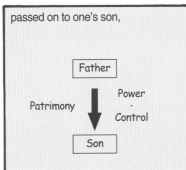

fundamentally, South and North Korea aren't very different.

If there's a difference, in North Korea, the father passed on an entire country to his son,

whereas in South Korea, the chaebol owner passes on his conglomerate, which is like a mini kingdom, to his son.

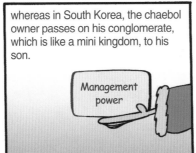

This extreme family-oriented ideology,

My eldest son, it's your turn to watch over the clan!

as evidenced by the shift in power from father to son,

Nobody to trust but family!

and the vertical relationship whereby power or property is passed down from father to son,

and the strong patriarchal system in which inheritance is conditioned on absolute obedience,

Since you've given up your studies in business administration, I've decided to turn the company over to your younger brother.

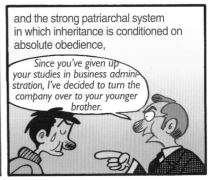

all exemplify the extreme temperament of the Korean people, whether they pursue capitalism or communism.

The Koreans have shown the world unparalleled examples of what

could be the products of their extreme nature.

Let's turn to another topic. How about Korean politics?

If you think of the country as a car, politics would be the steering wheel.

The steering wheel determines the direction in which the car will move.

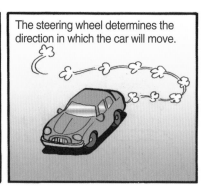

In the case of airplanes and trains with many passengers...

the plane or train moves depending on maneuvers made by the pilot or conductor, respectively.

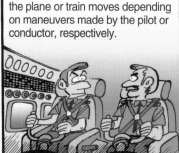

The lives of those on board depend on them.

That's why you see ambitious people jumping into politics.

Politics can be very complicated...

Each country has its own unique political circumstances.

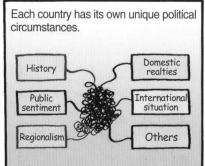

The more developed a country, the more stable is its politics...

The more undeveloped a country, the more unstable is its politics... so its people are bound to suffer.

But politics is a people-intensive business,

so variables like a country's geographical location, history and culture affect politics. Most of all, the temperament of the people has the strongest impact on politics.

Politicians

The people

politics

Therefore, even advanced countries do experience a degree of instability in their politics.

Yo! Driver! Speed it up!

Safety, my friend!

In Germany, where principles are said to be strictly upheld,

Eins, zwei, drei!

Principles

the people trust in their leaders, and there is not much corruption in politics.

This way ! Follow me!

Javol! (Yes)

Politics is very different in Italy where the people can be quite fickle and passionate...

Mamma mia!!

I can't stand it any longer!

The Italian cabinet has changed more than 100 times after World War II.

There's been a change in the cabinet again!

So what? Happens at least twice a year...

The Italians are very skeptical of politicians. They are even said to blame politicians for the rain.

How corrupt are those politicians to have the heavens cry on us!

The Koreans were forcefully colonized by Japan at the beginning of the 20th century.

After its liberation from Japan in 1945, there was a brief period (1945-1948) during which the U.S. operated a full military government in Korea.

US HQ

In 1950, the Koreans also greatly suffered from the Korean War.

boom

boom

boom

Adding to those sorrows, the South Koreans persevered through tumultous times after the war, including authoritarian rule by military regimes.

Evidently, Korean politics has crossed some tumultous waters to get to where it is now.

Korean Politics

Like other aspects of Korean society, Korean politics also possesses a degree of extremity that can be hardly found anywhere else in the world.

I will never understand that country.

KOREA

Let's address three examples, starting with Korean democracy.

DEMOCRACY OF KOREA

The concept of democracy was first introduced to Korea in 1945 at the time of Korea's liberation from Japan.

Democracy!

Huh?

Although the Korean independence was gained through another country, the U.S.,

the passion for democracy burned inside the Korean people.

Having democracy bloom in Korea is like... having a rose bloom in a bed of garbage.

In the 1950s, people looked down on us.

After many revolutions and struggles,

June 29th
Adoption of direct elections

Democratization!

Freedom!

May 18th
Gwangju Democratic Movement

No dictators!

April 19th
Student Uprising

unquestionably, Korea has now established itself as a democratic country.

There's still work to be done though...

민주주의 *

* Democracy

The French Revolution erupted in 1789.

Thereafter, other advanced countries struggled for at least 150 years before achieving democracy.

Anti-revolutionary forces

Revolutionary forces

But it took Korea only 50 years to get to this stage of democracy!

Democracy

If there's a country with a national income level similar to Korea's that has achieved democracy this rapidly, step aside please!

This is a prime example of that Korean mentality of going all the way, finishing what you have started.

Second example. Korean presidents.

The Republic of Korea was established in 1948...

Founding of the Government of the Republic of Korea August 15, 1948

As of 2002, Korea has had eight elected presidents so far.

One* was indirectly elected in a gym...

* Chun Doo Hwan

All of the seven former presidents have,

Park Chung Hee

Roh Tae Woo

Chun Doo Hwan

Kim Young Sam

Rhee Syngman

Yun Po Son

Choi Kyu Ha

without exception, experienced misfortune before or after leaving office.

The Fate of the Former Presidents:
Rhee: Died in exile
Yun and Choi: Resigned under coercion
Park: Assassinated by his intelligence chief
Chun and Roh: Incarcerated for corruption and sedition
Kim: Disgraced by financial crisis

Bang!

It's so appalling, neighboring Japanese reporters even said:

There's no other country in the world whose leaders have endlessly been subject to indignity!

Unfortunately, what this says is that the Koreans haven't had a leader they could truly respect.

How did the president become such a loser?

However, it's probably fair to say that, instead of these gentlemen not having been presidential material,

I mean... He must have had something. He was elected by the people...

there was just a lack of trust and respect for them on the part of the Korean people.

Give me a break! He ignored the will of the people and did what he wanted with the power!

Looking at the seven former presidents, we get some sense of

Not one president left office with the respect of the people.

the extreme and drastic nature of Korean politics.

Because we've been through so much in our history, maybe we're asking for too much from our leaders.

No, no... That's not it! Honesty is all we want!

Third example. The so-called 'Three Kims.'

Kim Young Sam | Kim Dae Jung | Kim Jong Pil

One of the Three Kims, Kim Young Sam, started his career with a bang in the 1950s, as the youngest elected legislator. He was just in his 20s.

I want to be president when I grow up.

He eventually realized his dream and became president in 1993.

3 Cheers! Hurray!

One other Kim, Kim Dae Jung, ran for president in the 1970s while he was in his 40s.

It's time for a young man in his 40s to lead this country!

He struggled for democracy and fought against authoritarian regimes.

Kidnapped in Japan

Accused of high treason

Accused of promoting anti-gov't organizations

Accused of being pro-communist

At the end of a long journey that was full of much hardship and heartaches... and even a death sentence...

You are sentenced to death!

bang bang bang

he eventually became president in 1998 and even won the Nobel Peace Prize in 2001...

NOBEL

The third Kim, Kim Jong Pil, made his appearance on the political stage as a key member of the May 16 coup d'etat in 1961 which brought Park Chung Hee to power.

On several occasions, he served as prime minister and ran for president.

Only the president is above me.

夕日照西天

He played an important role in forming a coalition government that brought about a peaceful transfer of power in 1998.*

We won!

Political power

Even after 40 years, he's still a major mover and shaker behind the Korean political scene.

I'm old school!

For a parliamentary cabinet system!

For conservative ideals!

Our purpose here is not to pass judgment on the Three Kims.

* His coalition partner was Kim Dae Jung.

These gentlemen dominated Korean politics for nearly 30 years...

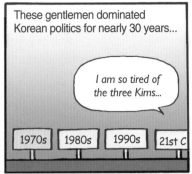

using their hometowns as their political bases...

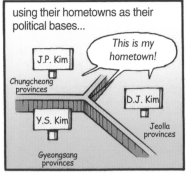

They took advantage of the regionalism existing among these areas, becoming the respective leader of each such area.

So-called faction politics is entrenched in the political scene,

which enable the three Kims to still exert a strong influence on Korean politics.

You won't find a phenomenon like this in any other, especially democratic, country in the world, where

regional leaders, with the backing of loyal regional supporters,

remain at the apex of power for so long.

Now, in North Korea, the father and son, Kim Il Song and Kim Jong Il, have ruled the country for more than 50 years.

You can see the extreme nature of the Koreas popping up in politics as well, right?

Yes, at least South Korea is a democratic country where all people are equal...

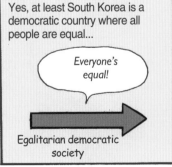

But, there's still a strong hierarchical power structure in place, a system hardly different from a monarchy.

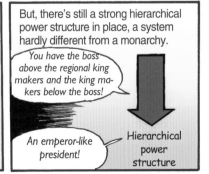

This kind of vertical power structure doesn't stop at politics.

It's also prevalent in business, government and even in the family.

It has become an obstacle to the realization of a true democracy.

The Korean people have endlessly struggled to establish a democratic society...

They possess a 'horizontal' way of thinking

based on the ideal that everyone is equal.

But there still exist 'vertical' (hierarchical) elements in society.

So the people have grown cynical about political and social affairs,

and have lost faith in their leaders.

What's the point here? What's the biggest problem facing Korea?

It's the collision of the vertical (hierarchical) social structure and the horizontal (egalitarian) way of thinking.

The only solution to this problem is the achievement of a true, genuine democracy.

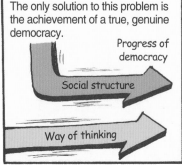

Okay. Let's now turn our attention to the Korean economy.

People often use the expression 'miracle' when talking about a country's economy.

Miracle of the Rhein River!

Miraculous rise of the Japanese economy!

The representative cases of miraculous economic recoveries have to be the losers of World War II.

... Germany and Japan...

But the nature of the Korean economy's miraculous rise is without comparison.

Let's first address the German and Japanese situations. World War II reduced Germany and Japan to ashes.

Let's take this huge sumo wrestler as an example. If he were knocked out by a stronger opponent, he may fall,

but with proper care and a couple of good meals, he'd be back on his feet in no time.

It would only be a matter of time before he's stomping away again in that ring.

The same can be said for the economies of Germany and Japan. Yes, they were knocked out after waging war against the rest of the world.

Let's take over the world!

However, the two countries were economic powerhouses to begin with.

And they did not become prosperous and powerful nations overnight.

Road to wealth and strength

In the case of Germany, it was a weak European country up until the 19th century.

The German people constantly suffered from hunger.

Potatoes were distributed to the German people during the 18th century to feed the starving people.

This all changed in 1870 when Germany defeated France, then a world-class power, in the Franco-German War.

This was the beginning of the rise of Germany.

Germany became unified in 1871.

With frightening vigor, the Germans started to build up their industrial and military machine.

Iron Chancellor Bismarck said,

With enormous backing from the government, German universities started pumping out talented people at a brisk pace.

These graduates became government officials, scientists and engineers.

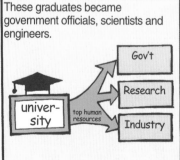

They were the driving force behind the new German nation.

Based on this national strength and advanced level of science and technology,

Germany was able to stand up quickly after being knocked out in World War I.

Economic resurgence!

In fact, Germany emerged as the strongest country in Europe before World War II.

Bring it on, brother!

But, of course, they lost again in World War II.

You dare try again?

Once again, however, with their large pool of talent and highly advanced level of science and technology,

coupled with the diligence and frugality of the German people,

Germany has emerged again as the strongest economic power in Europe.

Fierce people!

Yes. German to the bone baby...

Along with France, Germany's a pillar of the European Union (EU).

Put simply, Germany's economic power

is a product of having strenuously worked towards building itself over a period of 150 years since the late 19th country.

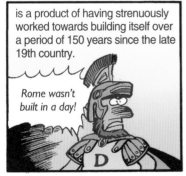

Rome wasn't built in a day!

Japan's case is no different.

Up until the mid-19th century, Japan was an isolated island country in the Far East.

They say there's this weird country in the Far East.

Where the people eat their fish raw, right?

Admiral Perry made his way to Japan in 1853.

Open up or I'll shove this down your throat!

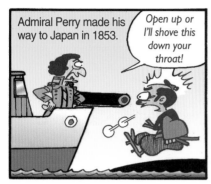

Japan was forced to open its doors.

All right... I'll open it!

The Meiji Restoration in 1868 changed the Japanese from head to toe.

They changed the political, economic and military systems of the country. The new systems were modeled after those in the West.

Based on a wealthy country, strong army policy, Japan was able to build up its national strength.

In less than 30 years, the Japanese defeated China in a war.

Sino-Japanese War 1894-1895

They shocked the world again by defeating the Russians a decade later.

Russo-Japanese War 1904

By this time, Japan had joined the ranks of world powers.

Konnichiwa!

In 1910, Japan annexed Korea. The Joseon Dynasty was overthrown.

This is our land!

Korean peninsula

The Japanese made a whole lot of money by exporting goods to European countries waging World War I.

Keep fighting! Keep it up!

MADE IN JAPAN

After the war, the Japanese economy gained momentum, and Japan's national wealth grew enormously.

I can't keep count of all this money!

On the other hand, the Koreans greatly suffered from the exploitation of the Japanese.

Meanwhile, the Great Depression hit the world in the 1930s.

During this period, after the army gained control of the government, Japan became engulfed by militarism.

A strong military must rise for the sake of national security and expansion!

Bang

The Japanese commenced a war to invade the Chinese mainland.

And, eventually, they started a war against the United States and its allies.

The Japanese lost the war after the Americans dropped the atomic bomb on Japan.

It seemed at the time that the Japanese would never recover.

It's the end for Japan...

But the Korean War (1950-1953) prompted the revival of Japan.

Boom!

Korean peninsula

In the 1990s, the Japanese were on the heels of the Americans, aiming to become the strongest economic power in the world.

USA

Now they're the second largest economic power in the world.

But, we're going through a never-ending recession...

Just like the Germans, the Japanese

Japanese economy

French economy + German economy

日本

built their national strength for nearly 150 years, establishing a firm foundation.

National strength

Thus, the Japanese situation was totally different from the Korean situation.

KOREA

Let's take a closer look at these differences.

Towards the end of the Joseon period, the Korean people led very difficult lives.

The 500-year dynasty was coming to an end.

Joseon Dynasty

In 1910, Joseon was eventually annexed by Japan, thereby becoming a Japanese colony.

The Korean people were thorougly exploited.

After its liberation from Japan in 1945, Korea was penniless.

You're free!

Did you say free?

To make matters worse, the Korean War soon broke out in 1950.

6·25

Whatever was left of the country was completely destroyed.

When a ceasefire brought the war to an end in 1953, South Korea was one of the poorest countries in the world.

KOREA

The poorest country in the world

Korea's per capita GNI at the time was a measly US$67!

Per capita GNI US$67

The streets were filled with beggars and people looking for any kind of work.

A dark cloud of despair hovered over the country. Hope was nowhere to be found.

How am I supposed to live now!

Sigh...

The Koreans, however, did not give up. They buckled up

I'm not giving up here!

and worked hard and saved up their hard-earned money.

Start work under the stars...

Return home under the stars!

For a better tomorrow, the Koreans worked at a blistering pace to get the economy going.

The Korean economy started its spectacular economic growth in the 1960s.

Korean economy

KOREA

Vroom

Using the justification 'dictatorship for the sake of development,' the military government put democracy on hold

Shut your mouths and do as you're told!

We need to put food on the table first!

and pushed forward with the implementation of aggressive economic development policies.

You can do it!

If it doesn't work, make it work!

The Five Year Economic Development Plan

The Koreans worked hard... so hard, in an effort to break free from the chains of poverty.

Looking for the good life

By 1969, South Korea caught up with the North Korean economy.

South Korean economy

North Korean economy

1969

And in 1977, South Korea's per capita GNI reached US$1,000.

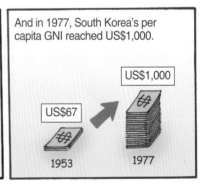

US$1,000

US$67

1953   1977

In less than another 20 years, South Korea's per capita GNI skyrocketed to US$10,000!

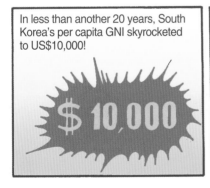

$ 10,000

Although South Korea's per capita GNI did drop below $10,000 during the Asian financial crisis in 1997,

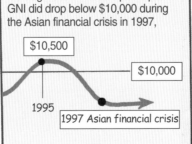

$10,500

$10,000

1995

1997 Asian financial crisis

the overall development of the Korean economy can only be described as 'a miracle.'

Korean economy

Korea's per capita GNI	GNP
$100 (1963)	US$2 billion (1961)
$200 (1969)	US$5 billion (1968)
$500 (1974)	US$10 billion (1972)
$1,000 (1977)	US$50 billion (1978)
$2,000 (1983)	US$100 billion (1986)
$5,000 (1989)	US$200 billion (1989)
$10,000 (1995)	US$500 billion (1996)
$9,500 (2001)	US$500 billion (2001)

That's incredible!

That has to be a record... a per capita GNI of US$67 in 1953 and US$ 10,000 in 1995.

He shoots, he scores! Goal!

High income nation

Korea's per capita GNI grew 200-fold in the span of only 40 years.

Until Korea...

the highest record for per capita GNI growth was 100-fold in 40 years.

The economic foundation that took the Japanese and Germans 150 years to build...

Brick by brick

Economic foundation

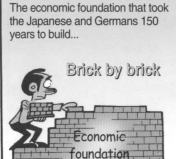

...the Koreans did in less than half a century.

I am superman...

Economic foundation

It's no exaggeration to say Korea's the only country in the world

Faster! Faster!

that developed so rapidly in so short a time.

The Guinness Book of Records

Today, China, with its 1.3 billion population, is developing at a rapid pace.

中國經濟 *

* Chinese economy

But in the 20th century, the title of 'miracle economy' has to go to the Koreans!

20C

The driving force behind this miracle

was the extreme, drastic, tenacious and unyielding spirit of the Koreans.

If we say we're going to do it, we will do it!

Will not quit till we see the end!

Meanwhile, the Koreans are the most passionate people in the world when it comes to education.

Scholarship has always been held in high esteem.

Those desiring to become part of the ruling class were required to pass a state exam known as the *gwageo.*

* Gwageo

Whether one was able to pass this exam determined the level of his success in life.

However, not anyone was eligible to take this exam.

Joseon society was characterized by a strict caste system in the following order:

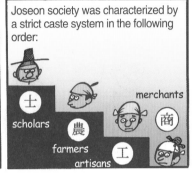

The upper class, also known as the *yangban*, was divided into civilian (the *munban*) and military officials (the *muban*).

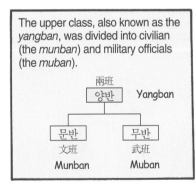

Although the sons of the *yangban* were eligible to take the *gwageo,*

the sons of commoners could only sit for state exams for technical and professional positions.

Government positions and the accompanying wealth and privileges were only reserved for the *yangban.*

Commoners and, in most instances, illegitimate sons of the *yangban* were restricted from sitting for the *gwageo.*

Thus, the *gwageo* was the gateway to success for only the privileged class.

But this changed with the fall of Joseon and the commencement of the Japanese occupation.

The class structure that had put the privileged *yangban* at the top crumbled to pieces.

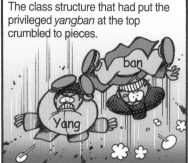

The social hierarchy collapsed and suddenly... everybody woke up as equals.

I'm a yangban!

Stuff it! You sold out the country!!

The Koreans suffering under Japanese oppression did hold token government posts.

City Hall Clerk

Token posts as they may have been, the Koreans could never break free from the notion that entering government service meant the good life... success.

Hot news flash!

And the breakdown of the class system meant that anybody had a chance to succeed.

Samdori got a job at City Hall!

You mean the son of farmhand Gaettong?

Only those people with higher levels of education could hold these government jobs.

We may be dirt poor, but we need to educate our kids at all costs.

Education was the only way to succeed – this education fever swept through the country.

In the old days, only the yangban could dream of becoming high government officials.

But now, only the educated will make it!

Poor farmers sold their cows and farms to put their kids through school.

Get your butt to school. That's your only chance!

Without regard to one's social status, there was now a chance to succeed in the new meritocratic society.

Everybody starts at ground zero!

Education was the only way out... the only way to make it in the world and bring honor to the family.

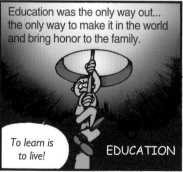

To learn is to live!

EDUCATION

This sentiment still runs hot in the blood of the Koreans. That's why the Koreans are one of the most passionate people when it comes to their children's education.

Education!

Education!

Education!

Going back in time... when Korea was liberated from Japan in 1945...

Korea

Japan

there were very few college students.

It's a college student!

I can't dare look!

If a student from a small village got accepted into college,

Old Kim's grandson got admitted into college!

the whole village would celebrate the occasion...

Go out and get the chickens and pigs!

We got us a future president here!

O' happy day! Party time!

As the Korean economy started to grow after the departure of the Japanese,

A new fatherland.

there arose a great need for qualified personnel. The number of students at universities greatly increased.

University

University

University

In no time, nearly everyone was headed to college. The number of college students explosively increased.

Number of university students

Soon, a college degree was not enough anymore to get a good job.

University Diploma

Job Guarantee

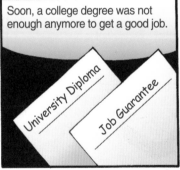

The doors would now open only to graduates of top universities.

I graduated from M University.

Uh huh... We'll let you know.

We'd hire S Univ. graduates, if we can help it.

Naturally, students were called on to endure the infamous 'examination hell' to enter top universities.

Pass or die

To survive this 'war,' the demand for extracurricular studies skyrocketed.

Extracurricular studies

Poor kids! How they suffer!

Moreover, in this Confucian society it was not enough to excel academically.

We must be human first!

There was also the need to refine one's culture and character.

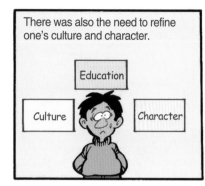

Thus, students also study such subjects as art and music to refine their 'culture' and 'character.'

If that's not enough, they learn Taekwondo and Judo to become all around students.

Korea is full of private institutions or *hagwon* that teach these extracurricular subjects.

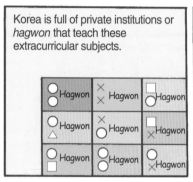

You'd be hard pressed to find an elementary school student that doesn't study with a tutor or go to one of these after-school institutions.

I'm having a birthday party and...

Sorry, can't make it. I have to go to hagwon.

Just call the ROK (Republic of Korea)... ROT (Republic of Tutors).

Public schools supported by the government

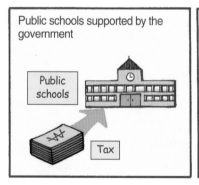

and private schools supported by tuitions paid by students are collectively referred to as

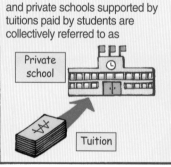

the 'public education' system, i.e., the elementary, middle and high school and universities constituting the basic educational system of a nation.

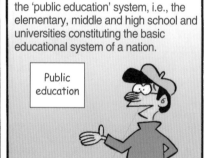

'Private education' refers to the additional education (tutors and hakwon) procured by parents for their children.

Now, the people of most countries harbor some complaints about their educational system.

We have big problems in our education system!

The same here!

We do, too!

Public education exists to enable students to become productive members of society after completing their basic education.

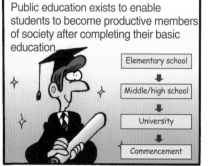

Why do you send your children to tutors even though there's the public education system?

I do it so that they can go to college.

Out-of-school studies is a requirement for that?

Well... I've heard of kids who made it without tutors but

everyone in my son's class resorts to out-of-school studies.

I don't want him to fall behind in anyway.

Isn't it hard to pay for all those tutors?

Don't get me started. We scrimp and scrape...

But... I'll pay for those tutors even if it means I have to scrub floors!

Although my kid may not surpass others,

I can't bear the thought of him falling behind others!

You see this survival and competitive instinct at work between neighbors.

So one tutor (or *hagwon*) gives rise to the need for another and so on and so on.

Tutor
Tutor
Tutor

This counterproductive and exhausting private system of learning through extracurricular studies continues with no end in sight...

Tutor
Tutor
Tutor
Tutor

Tutor
Tutor
Tutor
Tutor

Tutor

It is a product of the obsession of the Koreans to not fall behind their neighbors.

START

TUTOR

Where else in the world would you find people so extreme and drastic when it comes to private education?

TUTOR

Evidently, both the parents and the students are victims of an endless war of attrition.

All bunched at the finish line! Foul!

GOAL

The Korean unions are also known around the world for being extreme and drastic.

Compromise and concession? Those are words that hardly exist in their vocabulary.

Topple, pulverize and destroy!

Some foreign companies have left Korea because of these unions.

How's anyone supposed to do business with these unions?!

Once a labor dispute arises, there are typically union members who shave their heads.

FIGHT TO THE DEATH

Vic tory

They tie red bandanas around their heads and raise steel pipes and wooden clubs.

They wage an intense fight resembling warfare, throwing Molotov cocktails and rocks at the riot police.

We've also seen the extreme and radical nature of student demonstrations.

Down with this corrupt foundation!

Resign, you spineless chancellor!

When there arises a particular social issue or some complaint against a school policy, the students hit the streets.

Sights of students, for example, locking down the administrative building and the university president's office

Hurrah

Time for corrupt foundations to go!

Hurrah

We've taken over!

are not uncommon in Korea.

Why can't Koreans negotiate?

Instead of looking for a compromise through calm and composed discussions, why do the Koreans commonly resort to such extreme means?

Where did this extreme and drastic nature come from?

The Making of the Korean Personality

If we take a look at Japanese history, after the formation of the first state in ancient Japan,

Around the 5th and 6th century

the only time Japan was ever invaded by a foreign power was during the 13th century. The Mongolians tried it twice,

but failed each time.

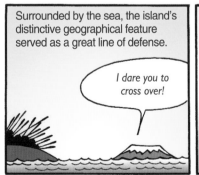

Surrounded by the sea, the island's distinctive geographical feature served as a great line of defense.

I dare you to cross over!

The Japanese people were occupied by a foreign power only once throughout their entire history.

That was immediately after World War II.

You get what you paid for!

Thus, there was no need for Japan to fear foreign invasions throughout its history.

Foreign invasion?

Not losing sleep over it.

Wars waged in Japan were essentially power struggles among those in the ruling class.

Who's going to be the top dog in Japan?

What about the Korean peninsula?

Throughout its history, Korea was invaded more than 3,000 times!

Ever since the formation of Gojoseon, Korea's first nation state, the Korean peninsula suffered from invasions by its northern neighbors.

Gojoseon

In addition to incessant invasions by various Chinese empires,

Do whatever it takes to put those Koreans in place!

Korea was plagued by invasions by the Japanese, pirates, the French, the British and even the Americans and many more.

Mongolia

Manchurians and others

China

Japan

United States
France
England

Japanese pirates

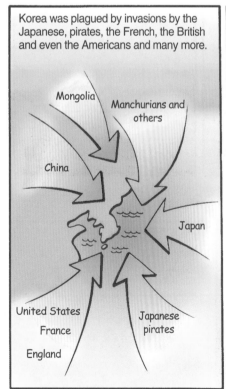

Korean history can be summed up as a struggle to survive from foreign aggressors.

The Korean people 'miraculously' preserved their independence

stick it

by not succumbing to even the huge empires that had conquered the Chinese mainland.

yippee~

Sharp survival instincts... pride... an unyielding spirit... all these qualities came to characterize the Korean people.

I'll die before giving up my independence and autonomy!

Now, as mentioned earlier, Japan did go through its fair share of wars...

But these were purely domestic power struggles... which were inherently different from wars with foreign aggressors.

Hence, wars between the ruling class were just that, a struggle to gain power.

I'm number one in this town!

The ruling class may have went at it with each other,

but it was rare for them to hurt the people

who were a source of tax revenue and loyalty.

Don't touch the people, the land and the crops.

They're all mine.

Naturally, the people could maintain some distance from the ongoing wars.

They're at it again.

In comparison, foreign invasions are by nature different.

Foreign invasions always entail plundering, arson and massacres.

Kill them all!

Take everything they have!

Burn what we can't take with us!

The people end up suffering the most, while the national wealth is drained.

In this light, evidently, a war on the Korean peninsula was not waged among the ruling class

Another foreign invasion? Oh, my god!

but against the people themselves.

Another foreign invasion? Start digging our graves. We're all dead!

Having suffered from endless foreign invasions,

what would have been the first priority for the ruling class in Korea?

It should have been the protection of the lives and property of the people,

but, in the face of insurmountable force,

the first priority turned out to be the preservation of the royal family and the state itself.

Thus, the preservation of political power and the government took precedence over the people.

After putting up a fight for as long as they could, if they felt they could resist no more, the royal family and all the subjects of the court would seek refuge at a safe place.

In other words, the ruling class would turn their backs on the people,

thereby forsaking a sacred duty owed to them.

There was a time in Korean history when the Koreans would successfully defeat and turn away even world class powers.

But when the Mongolians, the rulers of the world in their times, rolled into town,

being no match for the Mongolians, the royal family at that time fled to Ganghwado, an island off the western seaboard.

122

The royal family and imperial court fled and sought refuge while the people lost everything to the foreign invaders.

During the Joseon period, the unified China became too strong for Joseon to handle by itself.

CHINA

In order to preserve its security, Joseon submitted to the will of China.

If not,

the invasions will continue.

Ming

Later on, despite the waning of the strength of the Ming Dynasty and the rise of the Manchus,

Joseon neverthess insisted on maintaining its pro-Ming policy and refused to accommodate the Manchus.

Choong!

What is right cannot be changed!

Ming

The Manchus then invaded Joseon on two occasions.

Manchu Invasion (Jungmyo Horan) 1627

Second Manchu Invasion (Byeongja Horan) 1636

The Joseon royal family fled to Ganghwado and then Namhansansung.

HELP!

Gang-hwado

Namhan sansung

Joseon also suffered the same fate against the Japanese.

Korea looks mighty tasty...

The Joseon court paid little attention to foreign affairs, as it was preoccupied with domestic power struggles.

Finally, in 1592, the Japanese invaded Joseon.

The Joseon government hightailed to the northern city of *Shineuiju.*

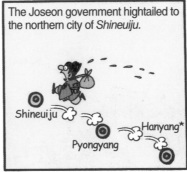

Shineuiju

Pyongyang

Hanyang*

With the ruling class gone, the people were left to deal with the ensuing disaster by themselves.

* Seoul's old name

History repeated itself in 1950 when North Korea started the Korean War.

The South Korean government broadcasted that its army was making great headways, marching on to victory.

Our ROK forces have crushed the communists and are pushing them beyond the 38th parallel...

However, the Korean government, which vowed to defend Seoul.

Trust the government and carry on with your daily work.

The government will do whatever it takes to protect Seoul.

blew up a bridge crossing the Han River to slow down the North Korean army's march towards the south

and moved the government to Busan, a city on the southern tip of Korea.

The government has moved its headquarters temporarily to Busan...

What?? They said they were going to protect Seoul!!

The people, who had believed in their government, remained in Seoul and suffered unspeakable consequences.

This is the price I pay...

for believing in the government!

In the vortex of all these hardships and foreign invasions,

what do you think the ordinary Korean people learned?

The king and the royal family will not protect us.

I am the only one who can protect my family and myself!

There's no one else other than myself!

The people picked up sickles and bamboo spears to protect themselves

and fought against powerful foreign invaders.

Let's rumble!

Let's fight back!

Not fighting back and just standing still...

means the end of everything, and only death!

yooo arrg

Now, how would the Korean people have looked upon

the ruling class that had turned its back on them?

They're always fighting amongst themselves...

and when foreigners invade, they run like crazy for cover!

They talk a good talk saying the will of the people is the will of the heavens...

But when it comes right down to it, party interest and self-interest come before anything else!

We'd be downright stupid to entrust those fools with our lives and property!

I'll protect my life, my family and my property with my own bare hands!

People unite!

Right on! United we stand!

The people living on the Korean peninsula, having suffered from constant foreign invasions,

lost faith in their rulers.

Politicians are all filthy scoundrels!

To stay alive, they united with their neighbors, thriving on a community spirit.

Let's unite to protect our lives, our families and our property!

This mentality, which is attributable to Korea's difficult history, still prevails among the Koreans.

We're one!

United we stand, divided we fall!

In other words, the Koreans have come to possess a very tough and headstrong temperament.

Do it!

In your dreams!

Their nature is to distrust, and not be obedient to, the ruling class.

Would you please do this?

I'll think about it.

Because the Koreans had to unite with their neighbors to protect their lives, family and property,

the Korean community spirit is stronger than that of any other country.

I cannot do anything by myself!

Good examples of this community spirit are the *dure* and *pumasi** traditions that originated during the Joseon period.

| Dure | Pumasi |

* Dure-Village-unit work force
Pumasi-Non-profit basis labor exchange

What was this *dure* tradition? It was the gathering of farmers during the busiest farming season,

I need to plant rice sprouts but don't have enough hands to get the job done!

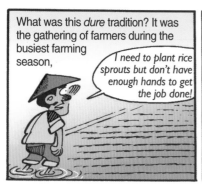

during which local farmers came together and helped each other out.

Let's think of a better way here.

If we do it alone, it'll take too long to plant rice sprouts and pull weeds.

We'll lose precious time and have a bad year.

So what I propose is that we start a dure and everybody from the village pitches in to plant rice sprouts and pull weeds. Wouldn't that be more efficient?

He means 'teamwork.'

Everybody in the village plants and harvests together, and we divide the profits,

Kim's rice paddy	Lee's rice paddy	Park's rice paddy
		Cho's rice paddy
Choi's rice paddy	Jung's rice paddy	

Kim's farm has 8 workers, Lee's 7, etc.

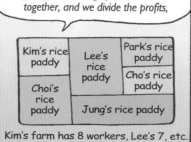

based on the size of the farm and the number of workers!

Good idea!

Dure was very similar to the Israel kibbutz or a collective farm you'd find in a socialist country. In other words, it was a village-unit cooperative work organization.

| dure | = | gemeinschaft |
| | | collective |

Pumasi is the exchange of helping hands during difficult times.

It's not as systematic as the *dure*, as it is prompted by *jeong*, or affection for one's neighbors.

Mr. Kim's short of field hands to weed his farm? I'd better go offer some pumasi.

It can be traced to the community spirit that prevailed in Korean society.

Unlike its literal meaning, 'to receive a helping hand,' *pumasi* does not refer to the furnishing of labor in exchange for a price.

pum	=	labor
asi	=	to receive

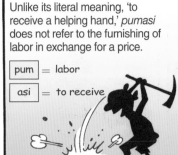

Instead, it is the bonding with one's neighbor, albeit within a limited scope compared to *dure*.

Skeptical about and cynical towards the ruling class, the Korean people united with their neighbors to protect themselves.

The formation of such communities was based on the horizontal way of thinking that became deeply embedded in the minds of the Koreans ever since the Joseon period

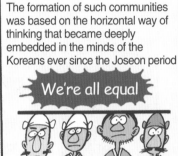

Coupled with the strong temperament of the Korean people, all of this led to the development of a spirit of defiance.

The Korean community spirit is best exemplified by *dure* and *pumasi*,

based on the principle that all members of the community are equal.

Any member deviating from this horizontal relationship...

either would leave at his own accord,

or be pushed out by the group...

Thus, a horizontal relationship between members is the premise for the existence of a community in Korean society.

In this 'everything's peachy when we're all equal' way of life, trouble stirs not only when one moves ahead,

but also when one falls behind.

Moving ahead or falling behind would disrupt the egalitarian relationship that is imperative in Korean society.

As extremely proud people, the Koreans are most fearful of falling behind the people closest to them, namely their neighbors and other members of their community.

Perhaps this accounts for the Korean proverbial saying, "If a neighbor buys a piece of land, I get a stomachache."

More than simply being jealousy about somebody close doing well,

it's more of a fear that they may be falling behind.

To the Koreans, 'falling behind' demonstrates to others their incompetence.

It is a loss of face to other members of the community.

This is why the Koreans guard their pride with their lives.

What do the Koreans hate the most? Words that poke and prod their pride.

Words that will discredit them.

128

To avoid being labeled as a cheapskate, the Koreans fight over the check.

You'd be hard pressed to find another country in the world where people fight over the check.

It's not like we're strangers. It would be uncouth to sit there and calculate how much we each owe. Right?

But, if one person pays for everything, wouldn't that be too much of a burden?

One person doesn't pay all the time. Everyone in the group takes turns...

At the end of the day, each person ends up having spent roughly the same amount of money. If my friend buys an expensive dinner, I could make up with two inexpensive dinners and so on.

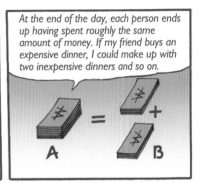

Taking turns on paying the bill saves face, and it helps strengthen the community spirit.

But there's always that one guy that goes for the shoelaces and ties his shoes while the bill's being paid... right?

We'd assume he was going through tough times and would forgive him a couple of times... but if this, 'shoe-tying technique,' continued, we'd kick him out of the group, accusing him of being a cheapskate.

Or we'd consider him a shameless person with thick skin who doesn't care about his reputation.

As you can tell, this community spirit is deeply embedded in the Korean mentality.

Even today, the *dure* mentality is still prevalent in Korea.

It's been mentioned many times before that this community spirit is a product of the Korean survival instinct.

Community

After all, it's impossible for a person to exist alone in society,

No man is an island!

Community

as everyone is recognized as a member of a community.

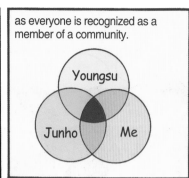

Being a member of a community inevitably means that certain parts of one's territory would have to be shared with others.

Common parts

This would entail the sharing with each other of spiritual and material 'parts' of one's territory.

Community

The Koreans call this common denominator of the community... *jeong* or affection.

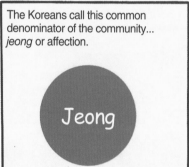

Jeong

The closer two friends are... the more common denominators they share...

Close friends   Not so close friends

The magnitude of this common denominator is the depth of their affection to each other.

Common factors = jeong (affection)

Between siblings = uae (fraternal spirit)

Between friends= ujung (friendship)

This unique Korean trait is something foreigners, even the neighboring Japanese, have a difficult time understanding.

There is a concept of 'affection' in Japan too, but...

The Japanese are not accustomed to encroaching on the territories of other persons.

Even within a community, the Japanese strictly observe the boundaries of others.

Me   A

B   C

Me

A   B

Japan   Korea

Even between the closest of friends, in Japan, as the drawing below shows, the circles would hardly ever overlap with each other.

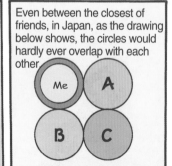

Me   A

B   C

On the contrary, for the Koreans... the larger the common denominator between two persons, the closer their relationship would be.

No big deal if a part of one's personal space is encroached upon,

as it would be natural for him to encroach upon the other person's space.

On a smaller scale, this occurs between friends,

and between neighbors

and at the workplace.

On a larger level, this generally applies to every Korean.

Now, let's suppose you refuse to accept these 'common areas.'

If you do this,

you should be prepared to suffer the negative consequences.

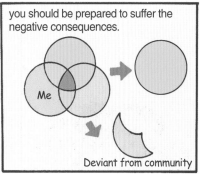

Me

Deviant from community

Meanwhile, the Korean community, which is bound together by *jeong*,

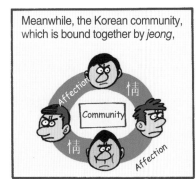

tends to be exclusionary.

Since the community exists not to attack others but to jointly protect its members from others,

outsiders are either the objects of struggle or indifference.

Although the community risks everything to fight for its interests,

when taken too far, the community may become self-centered.

* Not In My Back Yard

For example, the Korean community spirit may prompt the public to support the construction of facilities for the handicapped.

But, the construction of such a facility within one's community may be viewed as detrimental to its interests.

Due to their obsession to avoid defeat, instead of engaging in dialogue or attempting to compromise,

the Koreans tend to settle things by force.

This leads to endless disputes between communities,

which disputes often reach extreme proportions, especially when personal interests are at stake.

Let's consider as an example the conflict between the pharmacists and the oriental medicine doctors in Korea.

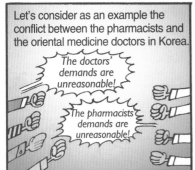

The doctors' demands are unreasonable!

The pharmacists' demands are unreasonable!

Although two groups may be similar in nature, their relationship with each other may be extremely antagonistic if their interests diverge.

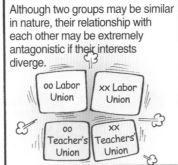

oo Labor Union

xx Labor Union

oo Teacher's Union

xx Teachers' Union

This is a product of the exclusionary mentality of each community.

In claiming one's share in a situation like this,

not being satisfied with this,

but demanding this will likely lead to conflict rather than compromise.

Since Korean communities exist to protect the interests of their members,

community

the more communities to which one belongs, the more protection would be available to him.

community

Many people join a number of communities not only for their protection but to secure a competitive advantage in society.

There are many Koreans who belong to a countless number of community groups ranging in all different sizes and natures. The more the better if one desires to expand his sphere of influence.

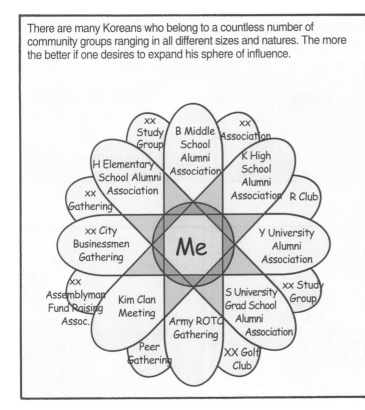

xx Study Group

B Middle School Alumni Association

xx Association

H Elementary School Alumni Association

K High School Alumni Association

R Club

xx Gathering

Me

Y University Alumni Association

xx City Businessmen Gathering

xx Assemblyman Fund Raising Assoc.

Kim Clan Meeting

S University Grad School Alumni Association

xx Study Group

Army ROTC Gathering

XX Golf Club

Peer Gathering

This is the modern day version of *pumasi* : helping each other out and, in the process, establishing connections.

Thanks!

I'm here to help!

On the other hand, these communities tend to be cliquish and exclusionary towards outsiders.

We must build this wall higher!

The community mentality is exemplified by school ties...

So, you're also an S High grad, huh? I'll help you out whenever I can!

Seonbaenim (Senior)!

Blood ties...

Did you say you're from the XX Choi Clan? We're related!

Oh, elder brother! It's my honor to serve you!

Hometown ties...

You're from xx City, too? Glad to meet you!

So am I! Take me under your wings and guide me!

Thump!

Cliquishness and cronyism are prevalent in Korean society

In this company, unless you're an S Univ. grad, they'll keep you down, brother...

Regionalism is also no joke in Korea, taking the home court advantage to new heights...

Everyone appointed to senior government posts is from that one region!

That region is ruling Korea!

It has been an obstacle to national harmony and progress.

Regionalism is a disease!

It must be cut out like a cancer!

This is what I'm supposed to say...

3K

A strong will and skepticism and cynicism towards those in power

Politics

Mistrust

Hmph!

are coupled with the exclusionary nature of the groups that exist to protect the interests of members.

Mistrust

Collectivism

Interestingly, even inside the walls of these groups, there can be found a strong sense of egalitarianism and high degree of competition.

We're all equal!

Never fall behind!

community

This gives rise to strong pride on the part of group members who have a difficult time accepting those who are superior to them.

This is my point... Nothing's acceptable unless I'm the king of the hill... The greatest!

Naturally, the Koreans have become the most extreme and drastic people in the world...

If I'm not to lose out to people close to me...

I gotta give it all I got!

It was in the 20th century during which the extreme nature of the Koreans intensified.

20th Century

What was the 20th century like for the Koreans?

After the Japanese slapped around the Chinese in the Sino-Japanese War in 1895,

they blatantly encroached upon Joseon on the Korean peninsula.

In 1896, the Japanese murdered Queen Myeongseong of Joseon.

We'll kill anyone who gets in our way!

The 20th century wasn't the dawning of a new era filled with hope and expectations for the Koreans.

It started out in darkness and despair, under the suffocating clench of foreign domination.

In 1905, Japan stripped Joseon of its diplomatic power through a protectorate treaty. Joseon essentially became a colony of Japan.

Protectorate Treaty

Korea suffered the greatest shame in its history when the Japanese annexed Korea in 1910.

* Joseon Dynasty

Although Korea had suffered from thousands of invasions before and was located right next to almighty China,

China

there was never a time when Korea had been annexed by another country.

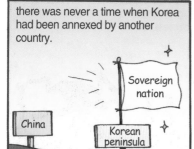

Sovereign nation

China

Korean peninsula

Hence, the 20th century started with Korea being deprived of its sovereignty.

Colony

Korean peninsula

It was a period during which imperialism prevailed. The stronger nations overtook the weaker nations.

Our Land

But the Japanese did something the Chinese had never done for thousands of years.

So to this day, it's difficult for the Koreans to stop feeling resentment towards the Japanese.

If Japan had understood the history of Korea and the temperament of the Korean people,

it would have thought twice about annexing Joseon.

Then, animosity between the Koreans and the Japanese would not have lingered on for this long.

This was a prime example of the limited experience of the Japanese in the international arena.

Until Korea was liberated from Japan on August 15, 1945,

the 35-year colonial period was a difficult time for the Koreans.

Even before the annexation, Korea was an impoverished nation.

And things got worse, of course, with the Japanese exploitations.

When the Japanese finally left, the Koreans could not have been any poorer.

Korea had hit an all time low as the poorest country in the world.

The joy of liberation lasted for only a brief moment before reality set in...

The Korean peninsula was divided into two.

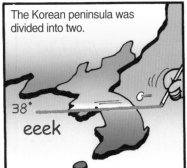

The Soviets moved into North Korea, while the Americans moved into South Korea..

The U.S. and Soviet Union respectively represented capitalism and communism, the bipolar ideologies prevailing in the world at that time.

The Soviet Union wanted to expand into Japan through the Korean peninsula to control the Pacific Rim.

Meanwhile, the U.S. was eager to prevent communism from spreading beyond North Korea. This also had implications for the security of the U.S.

The world's two superpowers split the Korean peninsula in half and confronted one another.

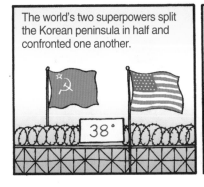

Suddenly, in the blink of an eye, Korea was the hotspot of the world where two opposing ideologies faced off.

Leftist and rightist ideologies divided the Koreans.

Murders, arson, assassinations, strikes and revolts...

Not a quiet day passed by on the Korean peninsula.

There was endless confusion and chaos . . . . .

Then, on June, 25, 1950...

North Korea made a sudden, full-scale attack on South Korea

The Koreans fought against each other for three bloody years.

Last year (1949) the Chinese Communist Party exiled the Nationalists to Taiwan and unified China!

If the Chinese did it so can we unify Korea under the banner of communism!

Kim Il Sung

Millions of people lost their lives during the Korean War.

An armistice ending the Korean conflict was finally signed in July of 1953,

DMZ

but Korea remains a divided country to this day, in fact the only such country in the world.

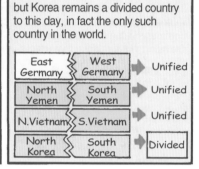

East Germany	West Germany	Unified
North Yemen	South Yemen	Unified
N.Vietnam	S.Vietnam	Unified
North Korea	South Korea	Divided

Even before the Korean War, the Korean people were already dirt poor...

No... No... No!

War

Water pail*

What little they had... the war took away, leaving the people with nothing but despair,

crash!

smoke and ashes.

We've got nothing left!

* A small gourd, frequently used by beggars to obtain food in the old days

Trembling with fear from the constant horrors of a seemingly endless war...

Free South Korea!

Unify Korea through force!

and suffering from constant hunger...

I'm hungry Waa Waa

grrrr

the Koreans nevertheless sought to prevail over their desperate situation.

I can't quit here. No. I'll start again and work my way up!

After the Korean War, the South Koreans filled their stomachs with the relief aid provided by the United States.

The unemployed filled the streets...

The government was incompetent and corrupt... the stench of corruption was everywhere.

Those in power committed election fraud to maintain power...

The people's cry for democracy were met with gunfire...

Hundreds of young people lost their lives...

All of this ignited the April 19 Revolution in 1960 that toppled the government.*

* President Rhee
Syngman was exiled to Hawaii.

Finally, free and democratic elections were held, thereby giving birth to a new democratic government.

The people hoped Korea had turned the corner, becoming reborn as a true democratic nation.

However, the voice of the people, which had been muffled by the ousted dictatorial regime, exploded in unison...

and the country continued to drift in a sea of chaos and confusion.

Unfortunately, the thrill of democracy won through blood and tears was short-lived...

as a coup d'etat was launched on May 16, 1961.

A group of soldiers led by a two-star general named Park Chung Hee seized power.

If we let this chaos continue, we'll all be reds in no time!

For a period of 18 years thereafter, the Koreans lived under a military dictatorship.

Park Chung Hee justified his dictatorship in the name of economic development.

Let's improve our lives! National reconstruction!

What happened to democracy?

Using the military and a secret police force, the Park government crushed the people's desire for democracy.

Putting food on the table is more important right now!

No time for democratic mumbo jumbo!

He desired to stay in power forever...

President Park Chung Hee must stay in power for life!

Park forever!

This is the only way to survive!

Park Chung Hee ruled South Korea for 18 years until he was assassinated by his intelligence chief on October 29, 1979.

To be fair, he is credited with having sowed the seeds for Korea's economic development.

Korean economy

He initiated the *Saemaul* movement, or the new community campaign, which instilled a 'can do' spirit in the Koreans.

The economic foundation that has enabled the Koreans today to enjoy a per capita GNI of US $10,000

GNI $10,000

was undoubtedly laid during Park Chung Hee's presidency.

Park Chung Hee's Presidency

Many Koreans today still revere and respect Park Chung Hee and his accomplishments.

His daughter should be president...

Does that bozo think he's in the Philippines or Indonesia?

tsk tsk tsk

Although history will remember him as the father of Korean economic development,

he quelled the voice of democracy by force.

Democracy...

Economic development is more important!

Economy

Nobody denies that the Park era was also a dark period during which basic human rights were suppressed.

We're busy exporting our stuff. So just shut up!

smack

He went after and crushed those people and movements that were against him

Demo-cracy

and set back the cause of democracy.

Democracy

Hypocrisy and

I'm doing the right thing, right?

Umm... Sure... Yeah... Totally!

He's so wrong it hurts...

distrust prevailed throughout society during this period.

Isn't this clown a KCIA agent?

Is he going to rat me out to the government?

The Koreans still haven't completely overcome the remnants of this period.

Hmm... Am I gonna get in trouble for saying this?

After Park's death, the Koreans had high hopes for democracy.

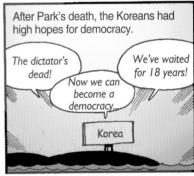

The dictator's dead!

Now we can become a democracy...

We've waited for 18 years!

Korea

Having said goodbye to the dictators, the Koreans believed spring had finally arrived.

Democrati-zation!

Spring 1980!

But this was a naive and fragile dream.

Dream of democracy

Events unfolded as the saying goes, "Power comes from the gun barrel."

Bang!

* Mao Zedong

On December 12, 1979, a group of army generals revolted against the existing military high command.

They brutally suppressed a democratic movement in Gwangju in May 1980.

A former general, Chun Doo Hwan, was elected as president in an undemocratic indirect election, marking the start of the 5th Republic. Chun was the leader of the December 12 insurgency.

The hopes for democracy were crushed again and another era of military dictatorship began.

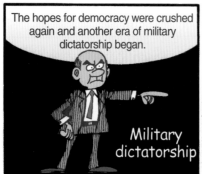

The new government that came into existence through the gun barrel

was fiercely resisted by the people throughout its seven-year term.

The Chun administration lacked legitimacy...

which prompted the military government to violently suppress dissenters...

Demonstrating students and workers flooded the streets of Seoul on a daily basis.

Tear gas filled the air of college campuses...

Finally, on June 29, 1987 the military regime relented and announced that, starting from the next presidential election, the president

would be elected through a democratic process, i.e., through a direct election.

Korea was caught in another whirlwind of chaos after the June 29th Declaration in 1987.

The unions that had been kept down and forced into silence

hit the streets and demanded higher wages and improved working conditions.

In fact, all the factions of society that had been harboring complaints against the government exploded at once.

Because of the inter-Korean conflict, socialism was never allowed to show its face in South Korea.

But it started popping up disguised in the name of 'equality' and 'justice.'

The atmosphere resembled the time immediately following the liberation of Korea from Japan.

But all in all... despite these side effects, one act of the Korean tragedy had ended with the June 29th Declaration in 1987.

Why? Democracy found its roots and started to grow at a very rapid rate.

The Koreans now enjoy more rights and freedom than ever before...

The power of the people is now such that... dictatorships will never be allowed again,

With the great advances of the economy, the Korean people have grown confident.

Korea successfully hosted the Asian Games in 1986.

Korea: 2nd in medal count

The world came to know Korea better as a result of the 1988 Seoul Olympic Games.

We did it!

Korea: 4th in medal count

Although the 20th century started out in a tragic fashion,

the Koreans can now expect a new era full with hope and challenges.

But, due to the 100 years of immense suffering,

Coup d'etat

Colonization by Japan

Fight for liberation from foreign powers

Korean War

April 19

May 16

Military dictatorship

Ideological conflicts between left and right

Gwangju Massacre

distrust, resentment and cynicism toward the ruling class have worsened...

Huff!

Oh gracious one...

...Yes, Yes... When I'm in power

... I'll give you a position!

You guys are a joke!

Govern-ment

After having endured colonization, war, revolutions, coup d'etats and dictatorships during the 20th century

the Koreans cannot erase the thought that they have been victims.

If I say what's on my mind, I'll only suffer...

To make matters worse, Korea's political leaders have taken advantage of the deeply rooted regionalism

Our region needs to control the government!

Good people, we have been ignored for too long! No more, I say!

Do you think we're a bunch of idiots!

This keeps people apart...

Quiet! That guy's from X Province!

Those Y Province guys always stick together!

Key government positions are held by persons hailing from the regional base of those in power.

Chief of Staff	XX Province
Chief Prosecutor	XX Province
Head of Tax Service	XX Province
Chief of Police	XX Province
Chairman of the Board of Audit	XX Province

As a result of all of this, it has been difficult to open the hearts of the Koreans.

A B C D E ···

가 나 다 라 ···

X Y Z W V ···

ㅈ ㅋ ㅌ ㅍ ㅎ···

In other words, the Koreans have come to possess a mentality with a double standard.

Like the Japanese honne or tatemae?

No... it's completely different.

What's a common phrase used by the Koreans?

To be honest...

Are you saying that the rest of time, you've been less than honest and frank?

Hmm... To be honest... you can say that....

Let's look at the general elections held in 2000 as an example.

Candidates

#1 Lee XX XX Party

#2 Kim XX XX Party

#3 Kim XX XX Party

Each of the major TV stations ran exit polls...

We asked people who had just finished voting...

Who did you vote for?

Voting area →

All the exit polls showed that the ruling party had won. All the major TV stations broadcasted these results.

All the exit polls indicate a landslide victory by the ruling party...

Ruling Party | Party A | Party B

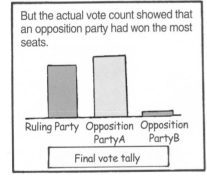

But the actual vote count showed that an opposition party had won the most seats.

Ruling Party | Opposition Party A | Opposition Party B

Final vote tally

Couldn't the voters be frank, if they already had cast their votes anyway?

I voted for the Party A candidate.

I voted for the Party B candidate.

Basically, the exit polls indicated that the people had lied about their votes.

Who did you vote for?

I may be disadvantaged if I say I voted for the opposition.

For the ruling party candidate.

Korea's probably the only country in the world where exit polls are inaccurate.

'Cause I don't want to pay for the consequences...

To sum all of this up, the Koreans have had a difficult history, especially during the 20th century,

20c

which has given rise to drastic and extreme elements in the Korean temperament.

I need to be this way to survive...

KOREA

Now, all of this generally applies to the older folks in Korea.

The Koreans in their teens and twenties have a whole different mentality.

Born starting from the late 1970s,

1970s

Poverty

they grew up without suffering from poverty and hunger.

They say North Korea's short on rice...

That can be easily solved. Why don't they eat pizzas and hamburgers instead?

Starvation report

They grew up during a period of affluence compared to the previous generations.

You need to eat!

No way!

They have enjoyed all the freedoms of a democratic society.

Thus, the dark sides of the previous generations are not found in them.

The Korean people are characterized by han (sorrow).

What?

Needless to say, they're less extreme and drastic compared to their parents...

Don't you have patience or any fighting spirit?

Why should I be patient? What will I use the fighting spirit for?

Korean youths are hardly different from their counterparts in the West or Japan.

We are young!

JAPAN   KOREA   USA

Communication between different generations is difficult, to say the least...

I can't understand kids nowadays.

Adults just don't understand!

However, the 21st century is upon us...

GLOBALIZATION

and these youths are the future leaders of Korea. Nevertheless, even this youthful generation possesses some of the extreme and drastic natures of the older generation. After all, they are all Koreans!

Extreme

Drastic

3

The Successes and Tribulations of the Koreans

1. The Fighting Spirit and Tenacity of the Koreans

made the impossible possible
but gave rise to anachronistic competition
and rivalry in Korean society.

The Korean people tend to thoroughly finish off what they have started.

This applies to drinking,

One more round!

That's enough.

Burp!

gambling,

I've lost the farm...

I told you to stop...

extracurricular studies

Tutoring costs 10 million Won per month?

We have no choice but to go all the way!

and also work.

I must finish this!

Let's call it a day.

Once the Koreans start something, they go all the way to get it done.

Quitting half way is

worse than not starting at all!

Korean immigration to America started around the end of the Joseon period, i.e., about 100 years ago when the first Korean immigrants went to Hawaii to work in the sugarcane fields.

100 years of immigration 1902-2002

HAWAII

However, overseas immigration started in earnest only in the early 1970s, so Korea's full-scale immigration history spans only about 30 years.

Let's start all over in America!

I'm sick of being dirt poor...

Meanwhile, today, there are no less than 2.5 million Korean-Americans in America!

There are bound to be some Koreans around!

Go to any place in America...

Bulgogi

Kimchi

Naengmyeon

LA   USA   NYC

The Japanese started immigrating to America around the same time as the Koreans.

Let's start a better life in the new world.

HAWAII

But, there are less than 1 million Japanese-Americans living in America.

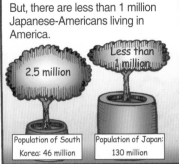

2.5 million

Less than 1 million

Population of South Korea: 46 million

Population of Japan: 130 million

Most of the Japanese have assimilated into American society, so it's difficult to find large-scale Japan towns in America.

During the Gold Rush of the 1850s, many Chinese laborers immigrated to America.

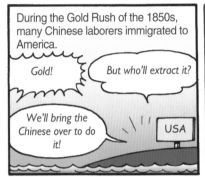

Gold!

But who'll extract it?

We'll bring the Chinese over to do it!

USA

They continued to immigrate to America to participate in the construction of the transcontinental railroad.

At the time, San Francisco was the port through which the Chinese entered America.

SAN FRANCISCO

The Chinese called San Francisco 'Gold Mountain' and built the largest Chinatown in the world there.

San Francisco

= Gold Mountain

金山 San Francisco

Thus, the millions of Chinese-Americans living in America have an immigration history of over 150 years.

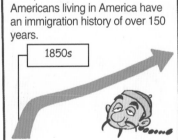

1850s

In contrast, in typical fashion, the 2.5 million Korean-Americans living in America have an immigration history of only 30 years.

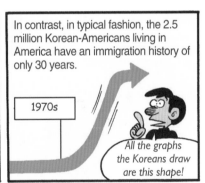

1970s

All the graphs the Koreans draw are this shape!

Currently, there are about 800,000 Korean-Americans living in Los Angeles.

Plaza Shopping Mall

갈비 ○○정 | 떡집 | 분식
한의사 | 안마 | 만화
머리방 | 순대족발 | 당구
해장국 | 부동산 | PC방

English need not be spoken around Olympic Blvd., the heart of Korea Town in Los Angeles.

Olympic Blvd

Hmm... Ollimpik-ga (street), L.A.-gu (district).

Many Koreans live in New York as well.

34th Street

STANFORD HOTEL

서울정 | 아리랑 | 점집

떡

Empire State Building's on 32nd Street and 'Little Korea' is on 34th Street.

As an incentive for helping out the U.S. during the Vietnam War,

the Americans contracted Korean companies to build many of the military roads in Vietnam.

The hard-earned dollars from working under the sweltering tropical heat of Vietnam

helped jumpstart the development of the Korean economy.

When the oil crisis of the 1970s hit and the world economy shook under the burden of rising oil prices,

enormous money poured into the coffers of the Arab nations.

The Arabs wanted to construct new infrastructure facilities with this newfound wealth.

Let's build a royal palace!

Also hospitals, schools, free apartments and highways!

Offering cheaper labor, and good quality,

Hmm... I see you did a good job in Vietnam.

Price seems OK. Skill level seems OK. Credit rating seems OK.

Korean civil engineering and construction companies promised to finish projects in record time, something which was unthinkable in more advanced countries.

You can finish this in 18 months??

Yes, of course!

So the Koreans did a lot of construction business in the Middle East and earned enormous hard foreign currency,

which fueled Korea's economic growth.

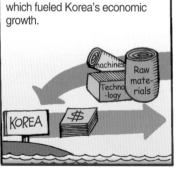

The Koreans went wherever work called, whether to the Sahara Desert or to the South Pole.

I'll go even to the end of the world!

Thanks to its workers who withstood whatever difficulties ahead of them, Korea was able to come this far.

If the Koreans had been picky about the working conditions, as were workers in more developed countries,

I can't work in the suffocating heat of the Sahara!

Those are not human conditions!

they never would have succeeded.

We'll pay you a lot!

Out of the question. I can't be away from my family for a whole year!

Compared to America, Japan and European countries which had built the foundations of their nations for more than 100 years,

ECONOMY

the Koreans started from the ashes of the Korean War,

NOTHING

throwing themselves into the game by banging their heads against every obstacle against them.

Kill or be killed!

With this fighting and tenacious spirit,

Nothing to lose!

We can do it!

and armed with the creed that nothing's impossible,

"Nothing's impossible."

We can do this! If it's undoable, make it doable!

the Koreans pushed ahead, using all means necessary.

10 chops, and any tree will fall.

If 10 chops won't do it, I'll chop it a 100 times, even a 1,000 times!

Let's look at Korea's POSCO*, the largest steel company in the world.

POSCO

At the time of its ground-breaking ceremony on May 1, 1970, there was no steel company in Korea.

No one imagined that, in less than 30 years, POSCO would become the largest steel company in the world.

* Formerly known as Pohang Iron & Steel

However, in 1970, Korea lacked the money to fund the biggest construction project at the time!

No country out there is willing to give us a loan.

The government diverted the reparation payments made by Japan for construction costs.

Here's the reparation payment for the pain and suffering you endured as a Japanese colony.

POSCO president Park Tae Joon and all of those involved in the process vowed to be successful.

Our ancestors paid for this with their blood!

*If we don't succeed, let's all jump into the Yeong-il Bay! ***

* The bay on which POSCO was constructed.

In three short miraculous years, they completed the construction works,

How could they have done that within three years?

Servicing Nation through Manufacture of Steel

and at 7 : 30 a.m. on June 9, 1973, POSCO's iron furnaces started pouring out red hot liquid iron.

It was the signal of the commencement of Korea's remarkable economic development.

Nobody in the world really noticed when the Korean steel and iron industry started in earnest.

Pretty impressive!

But how good would an iron mill built in three years be?

In less than 30 years, however, POSCO emerged as the largest steel company in the world.

During such period, in addition to the steel industry,

the Korean automobile, electronics and other industries have emerged as world class industries.

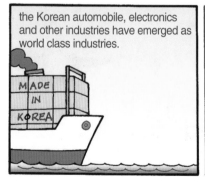

Safe to say, these achievements were possible because of the tenacity of the Koreans.

I can do anything!

The Korean spirit of 'going all the way...' was the driving force behind Korea's economic growth.

Help!

Can't stop the Koreans!

Squeal!

However, this tenacious spirit

often results in the disregard of formal procedures and principles.

Instead of opting for dialogue and compromise, the Koreans often go the extreme route.

Although Korea's per capita GNI has reached $10,000, old habits die hard.

The Koreans still bear the thought patterns and habits developed during its dark past.

There is conflict at all levels of society.

Now, competition is fundamental in any democratic society.

However, although the attaining of goals is important, it must be done in an atmosphere of fair play.

But there're many times when the Koreans ignore the rules of fair play and do whatever they can to win.

Let's say a foreign buyer comes to Korea.

Korean companies often engage in self-destructive price wars among themselves.

Politics is the area where communication and compromise are most lacking.

Politics is about power.

Power is a force that can affect not only the property but the lives of others.

In the past, the loss of power meant death.

But today, political power shifts according to the will of the people.

In Korea, however, a shift in political power

always brought about some form of political payback.

So, naturally, Korean politicians have fought tooth and nail to remain in office.

Korean politics, a prime example of the tenacity of the Korean people gone wrong, must be reformed.

The competition and rivalry for which Koreans risk life and limb

are counter-productive because such competition and rivalry are limited among Koreans.

The tutoring war!

All out war against my classmate!

I can't lose to him!

In the new global era, the Koreans should muster all their resources for use in international competition.

Instead, there's a tendency to give up on this fight and to concede that these foreign countries are beyond reach.

Korea is the weakest economic power among the OECD countries!

What can we do? Advanced countries are really ahead.

That's not gonna cut it anymore!

Korea can survive only if Koreans aim at becoming first! Look at you! Squabbling and competing with fellow citizens when you should be competing with the world!

This is no time to just compete against your fellow Koreans.

Instead, an era has dawned upon us where the competition should be against international players.

If I lose to these guys, I'm done.

We need to channel the energy that sparked the Miracle of the Han River toward the outside world, not expend it on domestic competition!

Korea is a country that produced its first automobiles by hammering out oil drums in the 1960s.

Thirty years later, Korea is now the fifth largest automaker in the world, competing against traditional automakers that have been around for nearly a century.

It's time for the Koreans to turn their unique fighting and tenacious spirit toward the outside world. A more rational way of thinking based on common sense and reason is required for this purpose.

2. The Hungry Spirit

exemplifies the spirit to strive for a better life...
and the endless greed of the individual.

There's nothing more painful than going hungry.

Grrrrrr

The Jews teach their children:

There's nothing worse in the world than poverty.

A person in the grips of poverty ends up shouldering all the agonies of the world.

"Compared to all the pain and suffering in the world, poverty is even worse."

He died without getting proper medical care...

"There're three things which harm people: worrying, quarreling and having an empty wallet."

"The body relies on the mind, whereas the mind relies on the wallet."

Don't worry about the check. Drink up!

He's very generous!

"Money blesses a man. Poverty ruins him."*

* The Talmud

The Koreans have suffered from poverty for so long throughout their history.

This was especially true during the period from the late Joseon period when the exploitation of the people by the ruling class was rampant

until the period following the Korean War. Poverty was thought of as a curse of the heavens.

Even the King himself cannot do anything about poverty.

That's life!

Every year, the people starved until the barley harvest season.

They were forced to eat grass roots and tree bark...

When will we be able to break free from this poverty?

Hopeless, the people saw no light at the end of the tunnel.

Poverty's my fate!

Poverty-stricken people often lack the desire and will to overcome their predicament.

There's nothing we can really do about it.

But merely having a strong will won't put food on the table.

I'm going to break free from this poverty!

Without any factories in place and with throngs of unemployed people filling the streets, there wasn't much the Koreans could do.

If a country does not develop its industries and create jobs for the people,

It's up to you now!

only a few crafty people will make a decent living.

The rest will continue to be poor, without opportunities to better their lives.

The first ray of light for the poverty-stricken Koreans

shined on them when Park Chung Hee started aggressively implementing his economic development policies.

5 Year Economic Development Plan	
1st Phase	1962~1966
2nd Phase	1967~1971
3rd Phase	1972~1976
4th Phase	1977~1981
5th Phase	1982~1986

Coupled with the will and effort of the Korean people, such policies brought about remarkable economic growth.

Let's live a better life~

Korea went from being one of the poorest countries on the face of the earth to the 11th largest economic power in the world.

The people desperately wanted to escape from the pangs of hunger.

This 'hungry spirit' arose from the Koreans' resolve to never go hungry again.

NEVER AGAIN!

HUNGRY

People around the world recognized the diligence of the Koreans.

The Koreans are the only people more diligent than the Japanese!

There's no change in that attitude despite the comfortable life in modern Korea.

Don't forget those times when we were dirt poor.

Of course, there are those who buy expensive foreign goods, and waste a lot of money on luxury items.

But most Koreans are industrious and frugal people who won't go near luxury items.

Frugality and savings!

BANK

They try to save more for a better tomorrow.

For a bigger house...

Children's education...

Household appliances...

Trips abroad...

This is exemplified by the fact that Korea has the highest rate of savings among any country in the world,

JAPAN

KOREA

UNITED STATES

Per capita savings

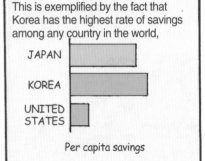

and the older generation's attitude toward leaving food on the plate.

You'll be cursed for leaving food on the plate. Finish it all!

The Koreans consider extravagance and lavishness as big no nos.

Have you lost your mind? How could you buy something so expensive without a second thought?

This is the 'hungry spirit' in effect... remembering the past during which they lived in miserably poor conditions.

We'll never forget those nightmarish days!

Of course, the younger generation that grew up during more affluent and comfortable times have a hard time blindly sympathizing with this 'hungry spirit.'

I just cooked rice. Why order a pizza?

Mom! Pizza tastes a whole lot better!

When I was your age, we didn't even have rice to eat!

Ahhh... Not that again!

I've heard it a thousand times.

Enough with that!

Kids today don't know the value of goods!

Parents... Every time they open their mouths, they tell us to save this, save that. But there's so much stuff!

Your cell phone works perfectly! Why in heaven's sake do you want me to buy you a new one?

All my friends have the latest models.

There's nothing wrong with how it works or looks... Use it!

I don't like the design. It's like so uncool to carry around.

No! If you change that thing every two years, this will go on forever!

Geeez. It's like talking to a brick wall!

Evidently, the younger generation lacks the 'hungry spirit' of their parents.

I'm starving.

Dieting is so tough.

Grrrr

Yet, what Korea has achieved today

Be strong sister!

Looking good is more important than eating...

is a product of the older generation's determination to break free from the chains of poverty,

Over my dead body,

which is characterized by the 'hungry spirit.'

I'm never going back there again!

Poverty

159

Who can blame them for that?

Nevertheless, the complexities of society demand that order and rules be imposed on economic activities.

As long as Korea has selected capitalism,

its people should comply with the rules of the market and engage in fair competition.

However, there are many of those who ignore the rules of the game.

Although the 'hungry spirit' has been the impetus to strive for a better life,

to some extent, it has deteriorated into a driving force for endless greed.

There are those who use every trick in the book and all means necessary to make money.

They abuse political connections and offer bribes for special interests.

There are always those fools that look for some recognition for having made a little cash.

The class system of the Joseon era has supposedly disappeared,

but there still exists a tendency to look down on merchants even in capitalistic Korean society.

'Anything's possible with money'... this love for money can be found in every corner of Korean society.

Many people worry that this amounts to pariah capitalism.

Pariah capitalism!

Pariah capitalism is a term coined by German sociologist and political economist, Max Weber.

Pariah capitalism. (Paria-kapitalismus)

It was a biting remark towards the Jews.

Money!
Money!
Money!

The word 'pariah' originated in India.

Pariah class

I'm sure you're all aware of the Indian caste system.

Caste (Class system)

Although many people have tried to tear down the caste system, it still exists in India.

Brahman	— Priests
Kshatriya	— Soldiers, Aristocrats
Vaishya	— Commoners
Shudra	— Plebeians

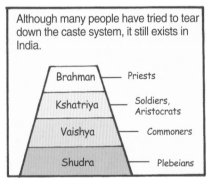

Now, the pariah class is so low, it does not even have an assigned place in the caste system...

The lowest class, like the Joseon era's baekjeong*

Like the burakumin before the Meiji Restoration in Japan.

Caste
Pariah

* a butcher

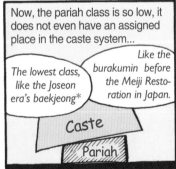

Without a country of their own, living in foreign countries and suffering all kinds of scorn and contempt, the Jews in Europe were often treated as a pariah class.

Dirty jew! Get him out of here!

Without a place to call home and without any possibility to rise in social status, the beaten and battered Jews

That's right! We've been ousted from our homeland and persecuted in every imaginable way!

looked to money.

Without land or power, what can we look to for a better life? Money and wealth!

Naturally, the Jews went to all extremes to make money, which to them equaled life itself...

I need to make money!

They engaged in either commerce or money lending

and developed a bad reputation as being loan sharks...

The Europeans generally despised the Jews.

But the Jews were indifferent to such scorns.

Well, indifferent is not the right word. Let's say they took advantage of such scorn.

Max Weber called this kind of behavior... Pariah Capitalism...

What about Japan? Commerce started to flourish about 300 years ago...

The Japanese people traditionally respected successful businessmen and merchants...

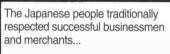

* Chairman

However, soaked in Confucianism, the Koreans have considered and still consider honest poverty a virtue...

In this light, many people today still look at businessmen with a skeptical eye.

Even the government doesn't trust big business and businessmen very much.

Why do you think there're all the red tape and the frequent government audits?

Many of these businessmen have become despondent.

In such an atmosphere, instead of looking to fulfill their societal duties and obligations,

it is easy for them to look for only personal gains.

You could say the people themselves are to blame for the continued presence of pariah capitalism.

Korea's made it this far because of the 'hungry spirit.'

But the 'hungry spirit,' to some extent, has deteriorated into an insatiable desire for money.

It's about time Korea broke free from the grips of pariah capitalism..

by complying with the rules of the market

and engaging in fair competition. It is time to strive for 'honest wealth' instead of 'honest poverty.'

A transparent form of capitalism must be established in society.

Of course, 'the hungry spirit' of the old days need not be forsaken,

but, instead of fueling personal greed, it should serve as an impetus to share with the hungry and needy.

3. The Education Fever

is the phenomenon that enabled Korea to develop a remarkable pool of human resources but that also brought about an endless war of attrition with respect to education.

Building an excellent, strong and righteous nation

is a duty entrusted with the people.

Isn't it obvious that countries with a lot of talented and qualified people are going to be well off?

Naturally, the Koreans have traditionally placed a strong emphasis on education.

The government has always emphasized education

* 100-Year Plan of the State

as its most important priority.

Receiving a good education and becoming a successful member of society is not only a personal triumph.

It also brings honor and pride to the family

and contributes to national development.

It's fair to say that the Korean education fever was the driving force behind the rapid development of modern Korea.

Once the ruling class fell and the privileged nobility disappeared with the fall of the Joseon Dynasty,

Korea transformed into a merit-based society.

-No Class discrimination
-Meritocracy

* Joseon Dynasty

Korean parents put everything at stake for their children's education.

Learning is the only way to survive! For you and this family!

They sent their children to college by selling off their cows and farmland.

Don't worry about us. Just study hard.

Armed with the 'hungry spirit,' these youths studied diligently, vowing to repay the sacrifices made by their parents.

I must do well for mother and father!

Despondent and in the throes of despair after the Korean War,

the Koreans realized the only way for a new and better life, the only way out of poverty, was through education.

Is there no way out of this darkness?

I must stand up again. The only way is by learning!

The Koreans burned with the desire to build Korea into an affluent country by acquiring the knowledge of advanced countries.

Yes, I will go study abroad!

Many Korean students left to study in America and Europe without so much as a penny in their pockets.

So long, my home! I'm not coming back unless I make it! Mark my words...

Studying in advanced countries started way back in the Shilla Dynasty (57 B.C.—935 A.D.).

I'm going to Tang China to study!

I see you've won a government scholarship!

Many students went to study in Japan during the Japanese occupation for the same reason.

Going to Tokyo to study!

Me, too!

Korean students studying abroad worked lowly jobs to pay for their education.

Get a move on it!

They studied through the wee hours of the night, fighting off sleep and pulling consecutive all-nighters.

They graduated and returned to Korea with the knowledge and skills learned from abroad.

Mother and Father...

I made it! I got my diploma!

During the 1970s, as Korea's economic development began in earnest, these highly educated persons made great contributions...

It's time for me to pitch in on the home front!

Furthermore, Korea's advanced education system pumped out well-trained personnel.

These locally trained personnel

We're the pillars of Korean industry!

School

Industry

and the overseas-educated personnel

Overseas talent + Domestic talent

joined forces to push forward with the development of the Korean economy.

Vroom

Korean economy

During the 1970s and 1980s, education became the fundamental stepping stone to success.

Success

College

High school

Middle school

It was the only way up the ladder.

Kim's son became a judge!

I guess selling his farm off for the tuition paid off!

Thus, the Korean parents' passion for education grew fiercer, to say the least.

We need to educate our children!

Even if we end up starving to death!

Education Education

Korea

As this fervor grew, so did the competition among all Koreans.

Of course, there were those like Hyundai Group founder Chung Ju Young who, for example, only received an elementary school education.

However, for most people, education was a prerequisite to success,

Although Japanese industrialist, Matsushita Konosuke, also dropped out of elementary school...

Matsushita Konosuke 1894~1989

so the competition for college entrance grew fierce.

During the 1970s, college education was reserved only for the so-called 'elite' members of society.

Hmmm... I'm thinking about going to college.

Quit dreaming! You never did well in school!

Only talented students went to college, and their college diplomas were their tickets to success.

Do you think just anyone goes to college? Even those with good grades barely make it...

College students were viewed as intellectuals.

The college students demonstrated again.

The government must've done something wrong for the educated to demonstrate like that.

But as Korean industries developed rapidly during the 1980s,

the demand for highly educated workers increased.

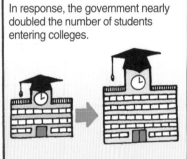

In response, the government nearly doubled the number of students entering colleges.

College education became available to the general public.

Hmmm... I'm thinking about going to college.

As long as you have the money for tuition, what's stopping you?

Naturally, the number of college students explosively increased,

I am a college graduate.

Now, it's more of a question of which college you graduated from...

Interview

resulting in cutthroat competition to enter top-rated universities.

Top Univs.

By the turn of the 1990s, college education became available to the general public.

Hmmm... I think I'll get a job.

You still need a college diploma!

As the number of colleges skyrocketed,

That's a university too?

Recruiting New Students

There are so many schools I've never heard of!

---

the gap between prestigious and nonprestigious colleges widened.

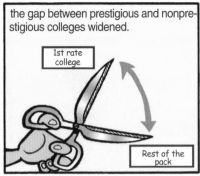

1st rate college

Rest of the pack

Whether one is a college graduate no longer matters. From which university he graduated makes all the difference.

Proud graduate of OO Univ.

Never heard about it...

Ahem!

Throughout society, the academic clique phenomenon has worsened.

That's right! Just shoot me! I didn't go to college. So what!

Academic cliques from prestigious schools have became tighter. They have become the new privileged class.

Unite!

Loyalty!

S Univ. Alumni Assoc.

K Univ. Alumni Assoc.

Not surprisingly, students must overcome extreme competition to enter the best schools.

To make this jump or not. That is the question...

Top college

Parents do whatever it takes to get their children into one of the best schools.

Run like the wind, boy!

The education fever of the parents has led to tutoring and extracurricular study wars.

과외*

* Extracurricular studies

By the way, Korean parents spent over 7 trillion won on extracurricular study fees in the year 2000 alone!

₩ 7,127,600,000,000
≒ 7 billion dollars

This is equal to about 31.4% of the government's 22.7 trillion won budget for education.

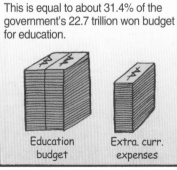

Education budget

Extra. curr. expenses

Needless to say, these expenses are an enormous burden to the Koreans.

If you add the costs of after-school private institutes,

private education costs would far exceed the entire education budget of the government!

Ex. Curr. Expenses

Private Education Costs

Well, what's the big deal if parents spend 7 trillion or even 70 trillion won if it's all done for the good of their children?

The problem is that despite the huge investments,

Extracurricular studies

the returns on such investments are very low, as exemplified by the low level of productivity.

Tons of money are spent,

but the system is turning out 'idiots.'

Productivity

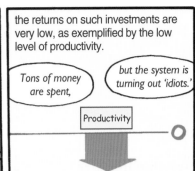

In Japan, the level of competition to get into college is no different than in Korea.

2/3 of all Japanese middle and high school students participate in extracurricular studies.

The most competitive, top-ranked school of each country is Seoul National University and Tokyo University, respectively.

Seoul National Univ. (SNU)

Tokyo Univ.

Each of these two schools are influential enough to impact the high school education system in each country.

SNU's entrance exam will test the student's thinking faculties...

Tokyo U's entrance exam will focus on testing logic...

Korea

Japan

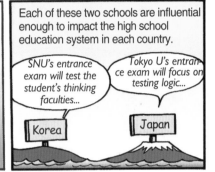

The graduates of these two schools are considered as the 'elite' members of their respective societies.

Influential in journalism and cultural circles.

Major political leaders...

Majority of congressmen

Majority of the heads of big businesses...

SNU*

* SNU's logo

They lead their countries in all facets of society.

Most of prime ministers...

Majority of congressmen...

Majority of the heads of big businesses...

Majority of high-ranking public officials..

Tokyo U.

However, why is big time Japanese journalist Tachibana Takashi vigorously attacking Tokyo University?

Have Tokyo University Students Become Idiots? By Tachibana Takashi 2001

The level of students attending the most prestigious university in Japan, Tokyo U, has dropped to pitiful standards.

We have kids going to medical school without learning any biology in high school, others studying engineering without knowing Newton's Laws!

Having reduced the number of subjects tested in entrance exams to ease the burden of students is creating arrogant, narrowly focused students.

I'm only interested in my major!

Major

Tunnel vision!

Tokyo U, which prides itself on being the best in Japan, is not even considered as one of the top 10 universities in the world.

And a survey run by the Asahi Newspaper revealed that Tokyo U students fall behind even students of other domestic universities.

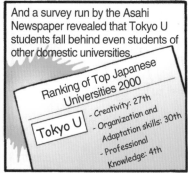

Ranking of Top Japanese Universities 2000

Tokyo U
- Creativity: 27th
- Organization and Adaptation skills: 30th
- Professional Knowledge: 4th

What's the reason? It's the high school educational system that focuses exclusively on the college entrance exam

Pass! Pass!

My only goal is to get into Tokyo U!

and those riding on the elite 'Tokyo U' brand who have neglected to enhance their competitiveness.

Some Tokyo U grads have absolutely zero skills and a whole lot of arrogance!

Even worse than its Japanese counterpart, SNU is not even considered as one of the top 50 universities in the world.

50th

There are those students having received perfect entrance exam scores who have failed. Many others are below average students.

How can such an 'A' student flunk?

'Cause throughout high school I memorized only what the tutors told me to.

Sigh.

This is nothing but the tragic result of the exam-oriented educational system and the extracurricular study wars.

Can't call that an education.

Look at you! You're just a test-taking machine!

Gag

We're all aware that new rounds of trade talks have started.

WTO

World Trade Organization

Globalization is proceeding at a much faster pace than predicted.

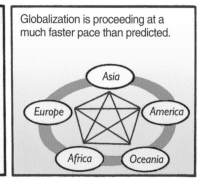

Asia

Europe

America

Africa

Oceania

Although only goods and money have been able to move across boundaries so far,

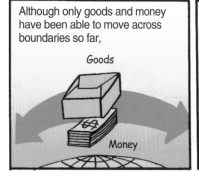

Goods

Money

in the near future, workers and services will be able to do so as well.

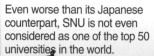

Workers Education Medical care

In no time, we'll see American lawyers, French doctors and English accountants working in Seoul.

Jean Pierre
Plastic Surgeon

Law Offices
of James Clarke

This means that the true competitors of Korean youths are not their classmates

but the youths of the rest of the world.

Society in the 21st century will be a knowledge-based information society.

Those with new and creative ideas will have the upper hand in competition.

Instead of nurturing and cultivating this creative spirit, Korean parents continue to be fixated on the entrance exams. They are consumed in the battles of this wasteful war.

Ultimately, if this continues, Korean youths will become less competitive than their counterparts in America and Europe.

What students learn from elementary school through high school

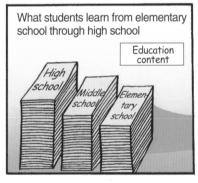

would fit only one CD-ROM.

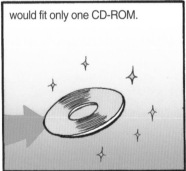

For 12 years, they cram their brains with this limited knowledge, which can hardly be classified as useful knowledge...

Such 'knowledge' is only useful once in their lifetimes: during the college entrance exam.

This kind of 'knowledge,' of course, provides little help in the competition against other students around the world.

It's an endless war of attrition with one student pitted against the other...

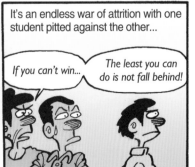

In agricultural societies, knowledge or secrets of the trade are passed on to younger generations through an apprentice system.

In industrial societies, knowledge is gained through endless and rigorous study.

This study leads to important discoveries and inventions.

In the modern information society where people are bombarded with information, there are limits on how much knowledge one may acquire through studying.

Thus, with a creative mind, it is important to assemble and combine various knowledge and information,

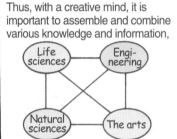

from which innovations are created.

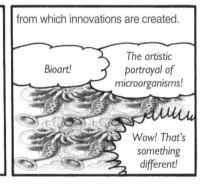

In order to do this, during one's youthful years, one must have been widely traveled, read and conversed.

Only then would one have accumulated sufficient direct and indirect experience that fuels creativity.

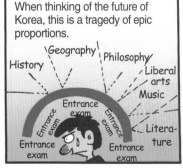

But the Korean reality bites! Students are forced to spend their golden years immersed in extracurricular studies for the sake of entering a prestigious college!

When thinking of the future of Korea, this is a tragedy of epic proportions.

Putting all this aside, there would be a glimmer of hope if Korean students studied hard once entering college.

But whether it's in Japan or Korea, college students are infamous for not studying...

During middle and high school, the students are chained down by their extra-curricular studies when instead they should be building their dreams and cultivating their ambitions.

By the time they enter college, the time they should be really studying, they go completely wild.

Freedom!

It's also a mystery to see parents end their involvement in their children's education once the college entrance exams are over.

Now it's up to him.

I've done my job as a parent.

Put simply, the Korean education fever is a misguided arrow.

The extracurricular studies in which parents invest enormous sums of money

Extracurricular studies

is responsible for reducing the competitiveness of the Korean public education system and its students.

HELP!

Students, who learn school curricula in advance from tutors,

If lesson 5 is being taught at school,

students would be learning lesson 10 from tutors.

This is the most serious problem of the secondary educational system of Korea!

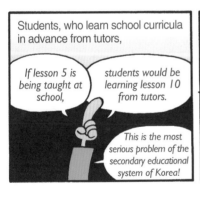

naturally don't pay attention in class.

Today we're going to study lesson 7.

Been there, done that, with the tutor!

Thus, disorder prevails in the classroom.

Bustle rustle

ZZZZZ

Classrooms are a circus.

Due to such a phenomenon,

The students don't pay attention in class because they've already learned everything from tutors!

That's because what's taught at school doesn't deserve their attention.

School | Parent

there is widespread dissatisfaction with the educational environment,

The Korean education system has collapsed. We can't depend on it anymore!

Whose fault is that? Come on! Who's the one sending their kids to tutors to learn subjects before they are taught at school?

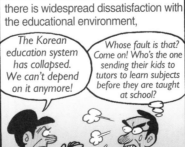

which has led to an exodus of students who leave to study abroad.

America, Canada, Australia...

KOREA

At last, I'm free from examination hell!

So, after all, Korean parents are giving away their hard-earned money to more advanced countries.

They spend money abroad in countries like America, Australia and Canada,

by sending their children to intensive foreign language programs during school vacations

and to foreign universities even after the students have graduated from top universities in Korea.

Studying in America.

KOREA

USA

Frequently, there are talented students who do not return to Korea after the completion of their studies.

I'm going to get my green card and live here!

USA

What's the final tally? Korea ends up spending huge amounts of money putting students through foreign schools but losing them anyway.

Hey! I made all kinds of sacrifices for you but what do I get in return?

The Korean education fever, which is known as being the hottest in the world,

Education fever

Ouch! That's hot!

should be rechanneled in a way that suits the changing times and society.

Slightly cooking it over a low fire produces the best taste!

The relentless pursuit of the anachronistic goal to enter prestigious universities at all costs

Yeke!

Entrance exams

has paradoxically resulted in enormous money and efforts being invested by parents to only cause the deterioration of the competitiveness of their children.

It's ruined!

To be fair, the education fever has greatly contributed to the development of Korea,

Education fever

but it is now casting a dark cloud over Korea's future.

For the first time in history, only 87% of admitted students decided to attend Seoul Nat'l Univ. in 2002!

This may be a sign of the changing times!

Not going to SNU!

4. Bread and Democracy : The Question of Leadership

There has been a strong dictatorship for the sake of development, but a lack of spiritual leadership.

It's a blessing for the people of a nation to have a great leader.

The importance of the role of the leader of a nation cannot be overstated.

We were able to avoid troubled waters because of the captain!

Depending on the performance of the leader, a nation can either progress or flounder.

Only a capable person with vision and exceptional leadership can guide the people of a nation.

Our country needs to go in this direction!

If the people respect and believe in him,

We can trust him.

He's a true leader!

the leader can formulate a national policy and move the nation in that direction with the support of the people,

Short and Long Term National Development Plans

as a result of which there may occur remarkable development.

On the contrary, let's say some grifter, a guileful professional politician leads the country.

You really don't need to keep those promises you made with the people.

They might get ticked off but they'll forget. They always do...

What happens in those countries where the people don't respect and follow their leaders?

What a total crook! Don't trust him!

He said he was going to honor the results of the primaries but he's running as an independent!

175

Confusion would arise, and policies would be unsuccessful.

Let's do this!

Do it yourself!

Policy

But how many leaders out there are perfect, satisfying all the conditions required of a great leader?

Character
Leadership
Scholar-ship
Decisive-ness
Integrity
Forbear-ance
Righteous-ness
Astute mind

This is especially true in Korea where the people tend to distrust their leadership.

Aren't there going to be problems if a leader lacks any one of those qualities?

It's hard to become a leader in Korea.

That being the case... many people attribute Korea's miraculous economic growth to the strong leadership of President Park Chung Hee.

Park Chung Hee
1917~1979

Park desired to rule forever in the name of national reform.

Power

Yushin (Reform)

Do not enter

He is criticized for having crushed all those people who opposed him and having greatly set back democracy in Korea.

Democracy...

However there is no doubt that, under Park's authoritarian rule,

Modernization of the mother nation!

Korea's economy grew by leaps and bounds.

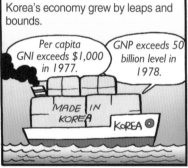

Per capita GNI exceeds $1,000 in 1977.

GNP exceeds 50 billion level in 1978.

MADE IN KOREA

KOREA

His leadership basked in the sunlight of economic growth while also casting a shadow over democracy.

Economic growth

Set back in democracy

Two choices were before him: bread and democracy... He chose bread...

DEMO-CRACY

I choose bread!

True, bread may have been a mere justification strengthening Park's dictatorial regime,

DEMO-CRACY

but there are many who recognize that his strong economic development policies, backed by his dictatorial power, enabled the Koreans to break free from the chains of poverty.

The situation confronting Park Chung Hee was to create an economic foundation from nothing.

The nurturing of industries became a top priority, and Park protected and supported businessmen.

Meanwhile, workers were expected to make sacrifices for the country.

They endured pitifully low wages, long working hours and poor working conditions...

The suffering of the workers reached extreme proportions.

But the police and army thoroughly suppressed the voices of these disgruntled workers.

A strong wave of resistance and defiance by the workers, students and intellectuals rose against the government.

There wasn't a quiet day during Park's tenure.

But Park enlisted all the great talents of the land and pushed ahead with his economic policies.

Against enormous opposition, he pushed forward with the construction of a national highway...

and nurtured various basic industries.

He was successful in industrializing Korea, setting the groundwork for Korea's present position as the 11th largest trading nation in the world.

People have become nostalgic of Park's strong leadership which gave rise to the foundation of Korea's remarkable economic growth.

He was a great leader!

In the meantime, of course, those who fought against his dictatorship for democracy are never to be forgotten.

Democracy

Without their contributions, democracy would not have blossomed in Korea, which would have then remained a land of complacency and suppression.

They kept the fire of democracy alive amidst the wild storm of the dictatorship.

DICTATORSHIP

Demo-cracy

Because of all their struggles, democracy was able to eventually burn freely and brightly...

Democracy

In the end, Korea was able to pull two rabbits out of the hat: 'economic growth' and 'advances in democracy.'

Economic growth

Advances in democracy

But the stronger the light, the darker is the shadow casted by such light.

Park Chung Hee

In the 21st century, Korea is witnessing disorder in its politics, which is headed by a lackluster leadership.

What is the reason for this? The hierarchical power structure of Park's era has weakened,

Power

Power structure

whereas, after long and endless struggles for democracy, the horizontal egalitarian way of thinking has grown much stronger.

Grow and be strong!

Way of thinking

Lately, the horizontal way of thinking has been prevailing against the hierarchical power structure.

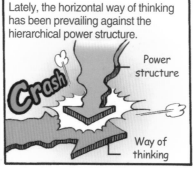

Crash

Power structure

Way of thinking

Ironically, there are those who are nostalgic of the strong leadership of Park's era.

We need a strong leader like before to push things through.

Do you actually think that's possible in a democratic society?

Since the death of Park, the Korean people have yet to find a leader of his caliber.

Maybe we should just import foreign leaders.

Of course, it would be fair to also note that there are widely divergent views on Park's legacy.

He was a great leader.

He was an evil dictator who dreamed of holding on to power forever!

After Park's death, President Chun Doo Hwan's* legitimacy was questioned throughout his seven-year presidency.

He crushed democracy

and stole the presidency!

* Chun assumed power after Park's death through a coup d'etat.

Chun's successor Roh Tae Woo*, criticized as extending military rule, was also unpopular with the people.

Another military guy will be president?!

Let's rid ourselves of these ex-generals!

What did I do wrong?

* Roh was also a former general like his predecessor Chun.

The 32-year authoritarian military regimes ended when a civilian government was inaugurated in 1993. It was the first civilian government since 1961.

Civilian government

Authoritarian military rule

The people fervently supported President Kim Young Sam, who led the new civilian government. At one point, his approval rating soared to 90%!

I'm going to put this economy back on its feet!

Hurray

But this honeymoon was short-lived. The new government was plagued by scandal after scandal.

Another cabinet shuffle!

Even the president's son is involved in a scandal!

New Cabinet Members

Towards the end of his term in 1997, Kim Young Sam was disgraced by a financial crisis which resulted in the IMF bailing out Korea.

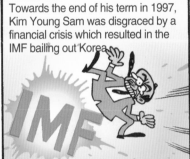

IMF

In 1998, Kim Dae Jung succeeded in bringing about the first transition in power between civilian governments in the history of the Republic of Korea.

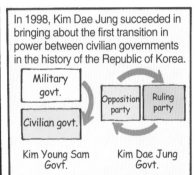

Military govt.

Civilian govt.

Opposition party

Ruling party

Kim Young Sam Govt.

Kim Dae Jung Govt.

He overcame the financial crisis through aggressive restructuring, successfully concluded a summit with North Korea's Kim Jong II and won the Nobel Peace Prize. He instilled hope and confidence in his people.

Kim Dae Jung attempted to restructure Korean society through bold reforms,

개혁

We are righteous!

* Reform

but many of his policies were pushed forward without adequate preparation.

Why are you just keep pushing forward without considering the consequences?

Aha! I see you're one of those crusty old liners!

There was endless criticism over the appointment of persons from his hometown to major government posts.

That's just too much!

We can only trust our hometown boys...

Scandal after scandal implicating high ranking public officials also shook his government as soon as it got off to a start.

Serious ethical and moral problem!

Can they act like that just because they have some political clout?

Kim Dae Jung's reputation widely varied from region to region. In other words, he failed to build a national consensus.

An overly ambitious guy who cares only about his power and reputation!

The greatest leader we've ever had!

Throughout history, the Koreans had been disappointed by their weak ruling class.

Humph!

This sentiment worsened after Korea lost its sovereignty to Japan.

What a total loser to hand our country over to the Japanese!

The cynicism and distrust of the Koreans toward their leaders have reached extreme proportions.

Everyone's in it for himself!

Nobody cares for the people!

From the perspective of the people, even a fairly capable and honest leader would hardly be adequate.

Trust me! Follow me, good people!

Does he really think we're falling for that one again?

Against such a backdrop, the leaders the Koreans did get, after the liberation from Japan, failed to live up to their expectations.

Your excellency, everything's just peachy!

They were largely clueless of the sufferings and hopes of the people,

Did you say the people are short on rice? Have them eat bread and noodles then...

Why do they insist on eating only rice?

having been surrounded by a curtain of people motivated by only self-interest.

Your excellency, you must never select this person for a cabinet post. He's got a bad reputation.

He's not part of our clique.

Naturally, the support of the people did not materialize.

Everything he does contradicts with the will of the people!

Why does he always go against the people?

Go home Ya' bum!

Most, if not all, leaders in modern Korea ended their terms amidst the cynicism and distrust of the people. They are largely remembered as failures.

Lack of support

Although the Koreans deeply distrust their leaders and are cynical towards politicians,

the flip side to this is that the Koreans yearn for a great leader,

Please send us a great leader. Is that too much to ask for?

a leader who would place justice ahead of personal ambition...

JUSTICE

IMPARTIALITY

If there was such a leader who could place the will and good of the people and the country ahead of his personal ambitions and desires,

most of his personal weaknesses would be overlooked by the Korean people,

He's got some weak points...

Yeah, but it's hard to find such a person!

who are prepared to give their undying support to such a leader.

Hurray

Hurray

Good examples of this mentality would be Park Chung Hee and Kim Il Sung, both of whom are deceased.

People have heavily criticized Park Chung Hee while he was alive.

We went through all this, right?

After his death, however, although the verdict is still out on the achievements of his administration, many Koreans say they miss Park the most among all of Korea's former presidents.

Whatever people say, there wasn't a better leader.

Old school is always better!

Why? He was, as we discussed, responsible for laying the foundation for Korea's economic growth.

Another reason? Although many scandals and cases of corruption occurred during his administration,

If you stick your hand in the water, it's bound to get wet...

bustle

bustle

KOREA

he himself was always considered a man of integrity and principles.

I haven't heard of any secret bank account or money laundering.

Nothing's come up yet...

What about North Korea's Kim Il Sung? 	He shut the eyes and mouths of the North Koreans and, by thoroughly brainwashing them, deprived them of their powers to reason.  *Because of our Father, the Great Leader...* *...we live in a constant state of bliss!*	He was a dictator that wielded power like an emperor.  *Where did that kid learn to say stuff like that?* *From the day they're born, they learn to praise Kim Il Sung.*

He was the very person who failed to accommodate the rapidly changing world,  Juche* Revolutionary changes	as a result of which North Korea is now one of the poorest nations in the world.  *I'd die a happy man if I could have just one bowl of white rice and soup filled with meat.* Grrrrr	The North Koreans have been totally cut off from the outside world and have been subject to brainwashing.  North Korea

* Ideology of self-reliance

They were led to believe that North Korea is a paradise and that Kim Il Sung, their Father and Great Leader, was a gift from the heavens!  *All hail the Great Leader!* *A hero for all ages, General Kim Il Sung!* *We're happy!*	What do the North Koreans think of this person who started the tragic Korean War and impoverished their nation?  *Communization of South Korea.* Korean War	They, in fact, still sincerely admire and respect him. 

To astonished outsiders, such a phenomenon looks absolutely pitiful.  *What a total freak of nature!* *Brainwashing is a scary thing!*	But who would know how much the Korean people, who suffered for so long under weak and incompetent leaders, 	yearn for a leader who can improve their lives?  *A great leader of the people...* *...but today the North is poorer than even...*

It's tragic for a nation and its people to not have a good leader.

The Koreans are eagerly waiting for a capable leader they can all respect...

But good leaders are not easy to come by.

A person elected as a leader after having politically matured in a democratic political system with the support of the people

would be able to garner their trust and respect.

Such a political leader could hardly fail.

The reality of Korean politics, however, is a far cry from this ideal situation.

The incumbent leader, who fears becoming a lame duck, delays the naming of his successor until the very last minute.

When the transfer of power becomes imminent, the would-be successors scramble to secure a competitive advantage.

They are bound to make mistakes,

which lead to a vicious cycle of distrust and cynicism.

The emergence of a trustworthy leader, that is the dearest wish of the Koreans.

5. Learn from the Japanese and the Americans!

Korean development was based on the models of advanced countries. But it now requires an independent model of its own.

The Japanese are said to be surprised of three aspects of Korea when they first visit the country.

First, the wide Han River running through Seoul.

Second, the spacious Korean homes.

*Wow! 56 pyong!**

* 1 pyong = 3.3m²

And third, the wide roads.

10 lanes!?

The Koreans can't really take credit for the width of their rivers, right?

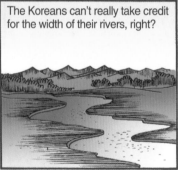

And it's difficult to compare the size of Korean homes to Japanese homes since the real estate prices are not comparable.

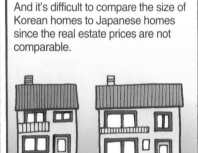

But how can one explain the reason for Korean roads being wider than Japanese roads?

Tokyo

Seoul

In Tokyo's case, during the peak of the bubble economy in 1989, an interesting analogy was uesd to describe Tokyo's land prices.

The price of real estate in Tokyo? More expensive than gold!

By selling all the land in Tokyo, you could buy every piece of land in America and still be left with money!

USA

Tokyo

With land prices that high, it's natural that Japanese roads are narrow!

Regardless of the fact that land prices are cheaper in Seoul than in Tokyo,

it's amazing that Korean urban planners considered laying 8-lane, even 10-lane roads, 30 years ago in the 1970s.

At that time, there weren't that many automobiles. It was unimaginable that the 'my car' age would arrive.

Why were 8-lane roads built when 4-lane roads would have sufficed?

It's because the urban planners who were involved in the process had studied in America.

* Southern part of Seoul which was developed after the northern part

Having seen the wide and spacious roads in America,

they predicted that one day Korea would also be flooded with automobiles.

They designed eight and 10-lane roads over what were, at the time, empty farmlands.

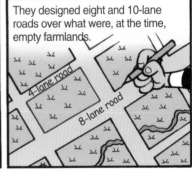

When Korea's economic development commenced in earnest, many Korean exchange students studying in America returned to Korea.

Many of them rose to prominence as policy makers in the government,

and transplanted U.S.-style systems and methodologies to all facets of Korean society, including the economic and cultural arenas.

Although American standards were adopted at macro levels in the Korean economic and legal systems,

Korean businessmen looked toward Japan for guidance.

Our situation is more similar to Japan's.

Japan was afforded the opportunity to reconstruct its economy through the Korean War that broke out in 1950.

By 1959, Japan had fully recovered from the wounds of World War II.

We're no longer a defeated nation.

The Japanese government started a 'double-your-income' campaign in 1961.

Because the labor movements are becoming so fierce *we should offer them a carrot.*

The campaign was successful, and the Japanese economy and industries grew exponentially.

The miracle of the Japanese economy!

The 1964 Tokyo Olympic Games, the first Olympic Games ever held in Asia, helped place Japan among the advanced nations of the world.

The Koreans looked at the Japanese miracle with envy.

I wish I was like that.

Around the time the Japanese started the double-your-income campaign, Park Chung Hee started the first phase of his economic development plan in 1962.

1st Phase of 5-Year Economic Development Plan 1962-1966

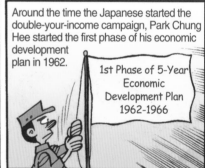

Although U.S.-educated persons were the brains behind Park's economic policies,

instead of relying on distant America for technology, materials and machinery,

the Koreans turned toward its neighbor Japan from which such resources could be obtained more quickly and cheaply.

Please lend me a helping hand!

Japan and Korea normalized diplomatic relations in 1965,

after which Korean businessmen commenced their interaction with Japan in earnest.

They learned technical skills, imported machinery

and even adopted Japanese management techniques.

Artisan spirit.

Lifetime employment system

Economies of scale

The zaibatsu system, which the American military had dismantled in Japan,

Because the enemies are so strong, we need to stick together!

系列

flourished in Korea under the name *Chaebol.**

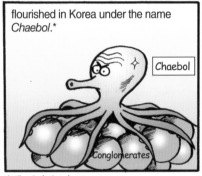

Chaebol

Conglomerates

* Chaebol: Conglomerates

Even the life-time employment system was transplanted to Korean society.

Solidarity · Cooperation We're one family!

Quality control and personnel systems were also imported from Japan.

Seniority system

Promotion

Since labor costs were cheaper in Korea, Japanese firms utilized many Korean companies as subcontractors.

Make it according to these specifications.

Of course!

Notwithstanding negative sentiments between the people of both countries, the Korean and Japanese economies became intertwined with each other.

Japan? No way!

The economy?

YES

Since there were many similarities between Korea and Japan,

the Japanese way of doing things worked well for Korea.

Korean economy

Japanese style

The remarkable development of the Korean economy up to the early 1990s was a product of

having successfully benchmarked U.S.-style policies

This is where we are heading.

and Japanese-style business and management techniques.

If that's the case, this will work the best.

Object economy

The successful adaptation of these two models

When approaching a hill, this is the way to do it.

to fit the Korean situation was the key to Korea's success.

When going downhill, do it this way!

The miracle of the Korean economy wouldn't have been possible without the American and Japanese models.

US model

Japanese model

But there were also drawbacks of having adopted the two systems side-by-side, the side effects of having an American head and a Japanese body.

Policy makers favored implementing U.S.-style policies,

Fair trade

Antitrust

Prevention of cartels

American style... American standard

whereas businessmen favored doing business the Japanese way.

Entertain customers

Diversify businesses.

Befriend bureaucrats

Make political contributions

It was not uncommon to see government bureaucrats and businessmen colliding with each other.

Why aren't you doing as you're told?

That may work in America but not here!

Inevitably, the two sides began to distrust each other,

Why do you insist on importing only from Japan?

He has no concept of the economic realities... Always spouting policies and theories.

and there has been endless conflict.

Regulation

Then in the 1990s, the world economy underwent a turbulent change.

Ahhh!

The currents are changing!

Globalization occurred at a rapid pace with the advances in technology, transportation and telecommunications.

Goods and services moved freely around the world without regard to boundaries.

With the onset of the digital revolution,

There's enough data in this tiny computer chip to fill an entire library!

the world underwent a fundamental change.

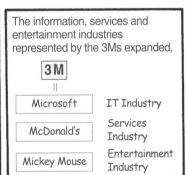

American capitalism stood at the forefront of the globalization of the world economy.

Rat tat tat tat

With advances in computer technology, the IT and BT revolutions commenced in earnest.

IT = Information Technology

BT = Biotechnology

The information, services and entertainment industries represented by the 3Ms expanded,

3M
=

Microsoft	IT Industry
McDonald's	Services Industry
Mickey Mouse	Entertainment Industry

thereby enabling the then-struggling American economy to once again dominate the world economy.

IT

On the other hand, Japan, which was setting its sight on overtaking America as the world's number one economic power,

Yo, America! I'm coming!

slipped into a deep recession in the 1990s.

plunge

Recession

Even in the 21st century, the Japanese economy shows no sign of recovery.

HELP!

The Japanese economic system, which was once the envy of the world,

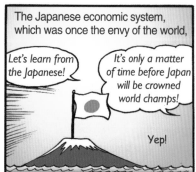

is now struggling to restructure itself amid a totally different world economy.

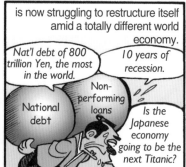

However, due to its very nature, it is impossible for Japan to undergo an abrupt reform process.

Above all, the Japanese people are slow to embrace change.

Meanwhile, the rapid emergence of China

is making the Japanese even more nervous.

Korea's situation in the 1990s was no different than the Japanese situation.

In the face of a changing world economy,

the Koreans remained complacent about their successes.

Irresponsible bureaucrats basked in unreasonable optimism,

while the financial system lagged far behind global standards.

Politically motivated 'parachute' appointments further hurt the financial industry.

Instead of focusing on technology development and quality improvement in order to boost their level of competitiveness,

businesses turned their attention to real estate speculation and irrational business expansions.

The price that Korea eventually paid for this was the financial crisis that engulfed the country in 1997.

Having been disgraced by the temporary loss of its economic sovereignty, the government regained its senses,

and instituted a fundamental restructuring of the Korean financial and industrial sectors.

However, the Korean economy is yet to fully recover.

The reason for the delay in the full recovery is often attributed to the unstable political arena and state of world affairs.

But the real reason is that Korea lacks a new economic model

to successfully cope with the revolutionary changes in the new world order.

The Japanese model, of course, worked well during the period of Korea's rapid economic development.

When the U.S. economy faltered during the 1980s, Korea increasingly relied on the Japanese model.

This all changed after Japan became mired in a recession, and especially after the financial crisis paralyzed Korea.

The Japanese lifelong employment and seniority system have created an inflexible labor market. It reduces the level of competition.

We need to follow the American standard. The new world economy is being restructured in accordance with the American standard.

We must benchmark the American economy and business principles! The only way to survive is by accepting American capitalism!

But the American economic model was developed just for America.

The economy is no different from an organism.

The economy of a nation must be tailored after the peculiar traits of the nation and its people.

The economy

and the land are inseparable!

There can be no economy without taking into account the culture of a nation.

Can you expect German perfectionism from the Italians?

Can you expect Italian passion from the Germans?

To be fair, the Koreans have achieved much by benchmarking the Americans and the Japanese.

American way

Japanese way

But the Koreans cannot be complacent with what they have achieved so far.

Korean Model

In order to accomplish its goal to join the ranks of advanced nations in the 21st century,

Advanced countries

Korea must go head to head with world-class economies.

No holding back this time!

The Koreans have a future if, and only if, they can come out of this fight standing tall.

Thus, the Koreans can no longer simply imitate the American and Japanese models.

It is imperative that they formulate their own model for the Korean economy.

No matter how well one can imitate a famous singer,

an imitator is just an imitator.

In order to become a top-class singer,

one must have developed his own voice and repertoire.

* Famous Korean singer

The stage on which the Koreans must now perform is before the world,

the world market where cutthroat competition is rampant.

To make a strong leap forward, Korea must break away from the old paradigm

and develop an information-based economic system that is suitable for the Korean economy.

What kind of paradigm, you say?

Well, let's leave that up to the economists! Shall we go on to the next chapter?

6. I am the king!

The desire to take the initiative, but the lack of the law-abiding spirit, characterize modern Korean society.

It is commonly said that the Koreans lack a cooperative spirit.

On an individual basis, each of them is smart and tough.

But, on a group basis, the Koreans are often accused of being uncooperative.

This way!

You're all wrong!

This way!

That way!

In contrast, on an individual basis, the Japanese may appear to be docile and even timid.

Hai! Hai!

But, on a group basis, the Japanese are known to act in unison under the directions of a leader.

But let's think about this. Who are the Koreans? They are a people who have survived a very difficult history without relying on others.

Having done that, why should I follow somebody else's orders?

In times of war, for example, the ruling class that was charged with the duty to protect the people was weak. The people themselves had to protect their lives and property.

Even democracy was won by the people!

With such a history and background, it is perhaps no surprise that the Koreans are a very proud and strong-willed people.

I am the king! Ha ha ha ha!

Moreover, we should take into account the egalitarian mentality of the Koreans: the Koreans just hate to lose.

Yikes! No way!

In the same light, they like to take the initiative and become the leader of the group.

It is difficult for them to submit to the will of another member of the group.

If everybody in the group wants to be the leader, the group would not be able to accomplish anything.

So whenever the Koreans form a group, a power struggle commonly ensues.

No surprise that they tend to be uncooperative with each other.

Surprisingly, there is one area where the level of cooperation is higher than anywhere else in the world.

It is the cooperation within a community based on horizontal relationships, a community with common goals and interests.

For example, if graduates of A High School and graduates of B High School clash against each other within the same community,

the prevailing camp will take all the spoils of the victory.

Naturally, a bitter winner-takes-all battle is waged between the two rival camps.

Such a phenomenon exhibits itself on a smaller scale at a personal level

and on a grander scale at a national level.

In other words, the Koreans take the lead when their interests are at stake,

giving everything they have.

When united under a common cause, the Korean people display enomous energy.

Doo run run run

That is, when the Korean people-who hate to lose, dislike taking instructions from others and delight in taking the initiative-

cooperate with each other, such energy is indeed explosive.

To the fight!

The explosive economic growth during the 1960s was a result of the collective effort of the Korean people.

The government's slogan to the people at that time was:

Let's live a better life!

The people strongly identified with this slogan, which helped bind them together.

I'm so sick and tired of being poor!

I want to live the good life!

The reason why the *Saemaul** Movement was so successful throughout Korea in the 1970s

For a new community

For a new community

* New community

was because its goal was acceptable to the people as a whole.

Modernization of the Motherland

I'm going to make the world a better place for my kids!

Although the Koreans emphasize the importance of the community,

Community

if their interests are not at stake, even the community itself is of little concern to them.

For the good of our country for generations to come...

Sounds good but it's a bit like reaching for the clouds. The present is more important!

But the Koreans roll up their sleeves and take the lead when there arises a concrete, practical matter affecting them directly.

Take the successful hosting of the 1986 Asian Games

or the 1988 Seoul Olympic Games.

The 24th Olympic Games 1988, SEOUL

Because these events directly impacted their future, the Korean people came together and cooperated

The streets of Seoul, which in the eyes of foreigners were always disorderly,

Honk honk honk broom

went through a sudden change during the Olympics, as the citizens of Seoul strictly abided by temporary measures to curb traffic.

That's right!

Odd-number cars only today.

Even the Koreans themselves were astonished by the sudden reduction in traffic on the streets of Seoul.

Uhh... This is Seoul, right?

Yeah...yeah... I'm still in shock.

Obviously, the unyielding spirit of the Koreans surfaces whenever they are forced to do something.

Do it!

Who do you think you are, ordering me around like that?!

The stronger the force, the stronger is the resistance. The Koreans are indeed a proud people.

Take this!

Force will never motivate the Koreans.

I've never come across people who are so tough.

The way to do it is to be gentle and persuasive.

What do you think about that?

I'll have to think about it.

After all, each and every Korean is a 'king' in his own right.

Ever seen a king taking orders? Think not!

This 'I am the king' disposition

motivated the people to rally under the slogan 'For a Better Life'

and it changed Korea from 'a land of despair' to 'a land of hope.'

But this disposition is often the cause of the lack of respect and consideration for others.

This phenomenon has worsened with the advances in democratization.

In fact, there are very few figures in Korea who are respected by the Koreans.

The level of respect for senior citizens and teachers in Korea continues to deteriorate.

Of course, the lack of respect and consideration for others

is bound to lead to disorder in society.

If the people are indifferent and disrespectful to their leaders, there is bound to be difficulties in the political world.

Politicians with such constituents are likely to abuse their power,

thereby leading to a collapse in law and order in society.

Another misfortune besetting the Koreans is the absence of a spiritual leader.

Who am I supposed to respect if I am the king?

There's another reason.

In other words, the absence of a father figure at the national level.

Role model

Paragon of virtue

This phenomenon is attributable to the disgrace suffered by the Koreans when Korea lost its sovereignty during its modern history. Such experience has deeply influenced the mentality of modern-day Koreans.

How could they expect to have a father figure emerge from such a shameful past?

Looking at other countries,

I truly respect you.

the Americans have George Washington,

The capital city is named after him.

Washington D.C.

Thomas Jefferson, Franklin D. Roosevelt, John F. Kennedy and many others whom they respect.

The American people continue to revere many of their former presidents.

Jefferson Memorial

Lincoln Center

JFK Airport

FDR Library

The French admire and respect Charles de Gaulle.

Charles de Gaulle

His name appears on monuments and airports.

Place Charles de Gaulle

Aéroport Charles de Gaulle

In Germany, there are Chancellors Adenauer and Erhard who are credited with rebuilding Germany from the ashes of World War II,

not to mention Chancellor Willy Brandt who laid the groundwork for the German unification. The Germans truly revere these leaders.

Ostpolitik *

* Foreign policy to improve relationships with the Soviet Union and Eastern European Bloc countries.

The Dutch revere the Prince of Orange, who led their independence movement.

Indepen-dence

They fondly refer to themselves as the Orange Kingdom.

We are the Land of the Orange...

We're not talking about the fruit!

The Netherlands

Even their football team is nicknamed after the Prince of Orange!

The Orange Army attacks!

Even though it is the portrait of their queen appearing on their legal tender,

For more than 50 years,

I've looked at this portrait.

the English truly respect historical figures who defended the country during times of difficulty.

Statue of Admiral Nelson

F

Admiral Nelson, Duke of Wellington, Winston Churchill...

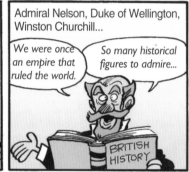

We were once an empire that ruled the world.

So many historical figures to admire...

BRITISH HISTORY

As for the Italians,

I'm the king of the hill!

Very similar in nature to the Koreans.

there are plenty of historical figures who deserve their respect.

There are figures like King Vittorio Emmanuele II and General Giuseppe Garibaldi, who unified the Italian peninsula that had remained divided for nearly 1,500 years after the fall of the Roman Empire.

In India, the Indians think fondly of Gandhi who dedicated his life to India's independence cause.

Gandhi! Gandhi!

For the Chinese, there is a man revered not only by the 1.3 billion mainland Chinese

We admire thee!
X 1,300,000,000

China

but also the 20 million Taiwanese.

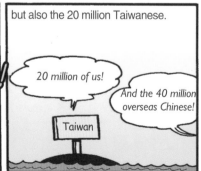

20 million of us!

And the 40 million overseas Chinese!

Taiwan

After the collapse of the Ching Dynasty, this man declared the 'Three Principles of the People' and founded the Republic of China.

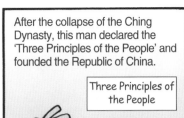

Three Principles of the People

Nationalism
Civil rights
Public welfare

He is Sun Yat Sen,

1866~1925

who was also respected by Mao Zedong and Chiang Kai Shek who pursued different ideological lines and maintained antagonistic relations with him.

Sir!

Sun Yat Sen is revered by all Chinese people as their spiritual founding father.

Meanwhile, the Japanese consider the emperor as a symbol of Japanese harmony.

However, the emperor is more of a figurehead instead of an object of reverence.

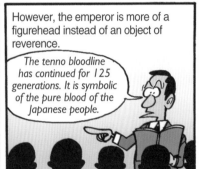

The tenno bloodline has continued for 125 generations. It is symbolic of the pure blood of the Japanese people.

Then who are the great men revered by the Japanese?

The Great Men in Japanese History

They are those who built the foundations of modern Japan, which, throughout most of its history, received little attention from the rest of the would.

Have you heard of that country where the people eat raw fish?

The Meiji Restoration of 1868, which was headed by these men,

Big time reforms!

established the framework for Japan's emergence as the second largest economic power in the world.

Japanese visionary Fukuzawa Yukichi who pointed out the way the Japanese should go

Fukuzawa Yukichi

1834-1901

and Okubo Toshimichi who established the bureaucratic system of government.

Okubo Toshimichi

1830-1878

And later on Saigo Takamori, known as the last samurai of Japan.

Saigo Takamori
1827-1877

I pushed for the subjugation of Korea.

Not to forget political heavyweight Ito Hirobumi.

Ito Hirobumi

I hate Ahn Chung-gun.*

* Hirobumi was assassinated by Korean patriot Ahn Chung-gun.

The Japanese love their heroes. They've built monuments for these historical figures and named streets after them.

大久保通り

壹万円
¥10,000

Saigo Takamori

To be fair, there are many historical figures who are revered by the Koreans.

Oh! How I revere thee...

King Sejong who promulgated the Korean alphabet and Admiral Yi Sun-shin* who commanded victorious battles against Japanese aggression.

* Navy admiral who won brilliant naval battles against the Japanese during the Joseon period. He was killed in action.

There are also Ahn Chung-gun, Yun Bong-gil, Lee Bong-chang, Yu Kwansoon and Kim Ku, who contributed to Korea's cause for independence from Japan.

Let us compare these persons to historical figures respected in other countries.

In the case of other countries, these historical figures greatly contributed to the development of their countries.

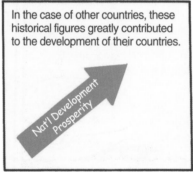

Nat'l Development Prosperity

In Korea, however, except for King Sejong who lived almost 600 years ago,

Characteristics of Figures Revered by Koreans

Resistance against Japanese

Martyrs

---

these figures were fierce combatants who sacrificed their lives for their country.

死

Admiral Yi Sun-shin	= Killed in battle
Ahn Chung-gun	= Executed
Yun Bong-gil	= Executed
Lee Bong-chang	= Executed
Yu Kwan-soon	= Died in prison
Kim Ku	= Assassinated

* All of the above persons fought against Japanese aggression.

During its difficult modern history, the Koreans were not blessed with a great leader deserving their reverence.

There's not a single road named after a president!

No memorials either!

It is questionable whether there will emerge such a leader in this day and age when the respect for the leadership in Korea is ever decreasing.

Respect

A recent survey asked students if they respected their teachers.

Among students surveyed from a number of countries, it was found that the level of respect for teachers was the lowest among Korean students.

In fact, such a phenomenon is widespread throughout Korean society.

Nevertheless, it would be an overstatement to say that Korea would never be blessed with a respectable leader.

If there was a leader such as Admiral Yi Sun-shin,

who would selflessly sacrifice himself for his country and people,

the Koreans would undoubtedly give their full respect and devotion to such a leader.

If Yi Sun-shin was reincarnated,

he would be hailed as Korea's 'national father.'

But, of course, that is a farfetched dream,

so we would have to hope for the appearance of a modern-day Yi Sun-shin dressed in a tie and shirt.

In order for such a leader to emerge, the cynicism and distrust prevailing in Korean society must be discarded.

4

The Long and Treacherous Road to Reunification

What would be the most ardent wish of the Koreans?	It would be the unification of South and North Korea...	The end of the cold war brought about the unification of all divided countries in the world except, of course, Korea.

Even Germany that was forcefully divided after World War II became unified.	In the case of Korea, the country was also forcefully divided without regard to the will of the Korean people.	Today, Korea remains as the only divided country in the world.
		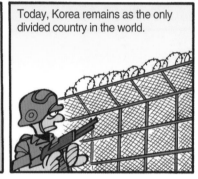

The reality is that no one can guess when unification will occur.	To this date, South and North Korea have failed to sign a peace treaty.	Ever since a ceasefire agreement was reached in 1953,

the two Koreas have walked a tight rope to avoid going back to war.	As the four powers surrounding the Korean peninsula, i.e., the U.S., Russia, China and Japan, have keen interests in Korea,	peace on the Korean peninsula has always attracted worldwide attention.

206

A unified Korea would have a

Reunified Korea

combined population of 70 million.

Germany	80 mil
England	65 mil
France	55 mil
Italy	50 mil
Japan	126 mil

The combination of South Korea's capital and technology with North Korea's natural resources and labor force

Labor + Capital + Technology

would propel the unified Korea into the ranks of major Asian powerhouses.

If Korea diverts its astronomical combined defense budget to finance other worthy causes,

$ $

Defense budget

it could emerge as one of the strongest nations in the world.

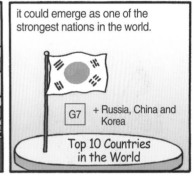

G7 + Russia, China and Korea

Top 10 Countries in the World

Unification is absolutely required in order for Korea to make a giant leap forward in the 21st century.

Unification

It is also what the Koreans dearly aspire for in their hearts.

After the unification of the Three Kingdoms by Shilla in 676, the Korean peninsula remained as a unified state for nearly 1,300 years.

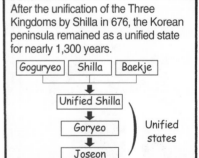

Goguryeo | Shilla | Baekje

↓

Unified Shilla

↓

Goryeo

↓

Joseon

Unified states

But half a century has already elapsed since the division of Korea in 1945.

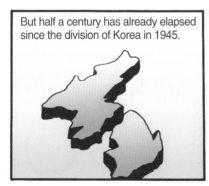

If unification is so important and endearing to the Koreans,

Reunification!

North   South

why does it seem like such a farfetched and difficult goal to achieve at this time?

NO!

TV

Letters

Radio

Telephone

Let's examine the unification issue and see why there lies ahead such a treacherous road.

The circumstances surrounding the split of a family is complex enough.

Imagine the magnitude of the complexity of the circumstances surrounding the split of an entire nation.

The division of a nation may be classified into a number of patterns.

In the case a particular nation becomes so strong to the extent that it starts posing a threat to neighboring countries,

Everybody on your knees!

superpowers may intervene and forcefully divide such a nation. This is known as an 'external-force-driven division.'

We'll have to separate you two!

Meanwhile, in the case the people of a particular nation engage in endless conflict,

a byproduct of such conflict may be the division of the nation. This is known as an 'internal-conflict-driven division.'

I can't stand another day with you!

The victors of World War II forcefully divided Germany after the war ended with Germany's defeat.

If we leave them alone,

they're bound to start another war.

Hence, a representative case of an 'external-force-driven division' occurred in Germany.

West Germany   East Germany

In the case of Korea, the country was divided by the U.S. and the Soviet Union after World War II, without regard to the will of the Korean people.

USSR

38th Parallel

US

Thus, the division of Korea is also an 'external-force-driven division.'

USSR

North Korea

South Korea

US

To make matters worse, after the liberation from Japan, ideological battles raged throughout Korea.

The country was torn apart by different ideologies.

In the case of Korea, the country's division was the product of both internal conflict and external force.

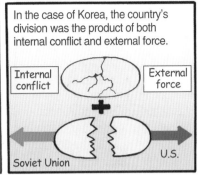

Undoubtedly, the Korean situation is much more complex than the German situation.

On top of everything else, the Korean War further complicated the Korean situation.

The end product of all of this was the drawing of a ceasefire line through Korea...

and a deep hatred and distrust between the North and South.

In contrast, despite having been forcefully divided,

there was no reason for West and East Germany to go to war with each other. Hence, there existed little, if any, enmity between West and East Germany.

In other words, the common identity of the Germans was left intact, since, when the opportune time arrived, the two Germanies would unify.

In fact, the West Germans freely traveled throughout East Germany,

while East Germans watched West German TV broadcasts. The exchange between the two sides was not severed.

Once the communist regime fell, West and East Germany could proceed to unification right away.

On the contrary, among communist countries, North Korea has adhered to the most extreme form of Stalinism,

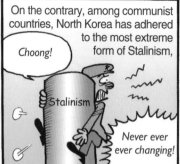

while South Korea adopted a strict anti-communist policy after having undergone the tragedies of the Korean War.

Thus, the two Koreas have become far out of reach from each other.

The prolonged division for more than 50 years, during which even no phone calls or letters were allowed to be exchanged, caused

North and South Korea to drift apart to such an extent that they have become totally different societies.

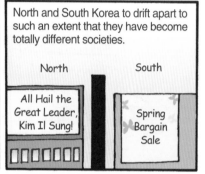

In addition, North Korea continues insisting on realizing unification through the communization of South Korea,

while, of course, South Korea continues rejecting such an idea.

Thus, the two Koreas are yet to have a meeting of the minds on even the most basic first step to unification.

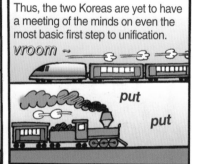

Nevertheless, neither side can afford to give up on this most important goal.

So the South insists on pursuing unification in accordance with its plan and vice versa.

Let's see how these plans differ,

by first taking a look at the South Korean plan.

South Korea's Plan for Unification

With the fall of the Eastern European Bloc in 1989, the cold war was brought to an end.

It's the economy, stupid!

Ideological conflict

Accordingly, South Korea's policy on North Korea also underwent a significant change.

So far, we've considered the North Koreans to be only the objects of confrontation and hostility.

We may be divided but the 70 million Koreans living on the peninsula are all members of the same community.

The two Koreas must restore and develop the national community through open exchanges and cooperation based on the principle of co-existence and co-prosperity.

Ehh?

South Korea's new policy on North Korea was dubbed the 'Korean Community Unification Plan.'

Korean Community Unification Plan

Sept. 11, 1989

There are three principles that are conditions precedent to the implementation of this unification plan.

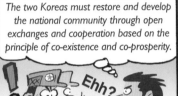

Autonomy

Peace   Democracy

Autonomy Since unification is a matter to be resolved by the Koreans,

This is a matter to be resolved by the Koreans only.

Unification

any decisions regarding the matter must be made by the Koreans themselves without the intervention of outside forces.

Why should outsiders be involved?

Yes! It's a matter of national pride!

Peace Having suffered unspeakable horrors during the Korean War,

Korean War

it is imperative that the two Koreas reject any attempts to resort to force and violence in the unification process,

NEVER!

so that unification may be achieved through peaceful means.

What's the use of unification if we have to spill blood again!

Democracy

All processes for unification

must be undertaken in accordance with democratic principles and procedures.

Reunification

Democratic procedures, methodology and consensus

That is, all men and women are to be guaranteed the freedom and right to live their lives as human beings.

Unified country

Under this principle,

That's unacceptable!

Ruling class

People

it would be unacceptable for North Korea to continue to insist upon dictatorial rule by the Communist Party.

Dictatorial rule by the proletariat class and the Communist Party!

It is a principle that clearly refuses to accommodate North Korea's policy to achieve unification through communization.

That's not happening! Nope!

Communi-zation

The crux of the Korean Community Unification Plan is the formation of a transitory coalition between South and North Korea.

South - North Coalition

As a matter of course, there would be

The Father Leader has ordered an increase in production!

When will the stock market go back up?

North Korea

South Korea

unimaginable disorder and chaos if the two Koreas are unified overnight.

Thus, there is an absolute need for a transitory stage to ease the severe impact of unification.

Division

Transitory stage

Unification

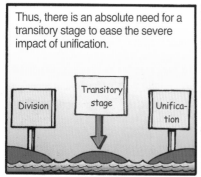

After forming a transitory coalition as a stepping stone to unification,

Division → South-North Coalition → Unification

(Transitory stage)

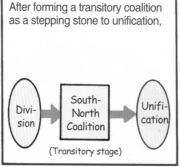

the Koreans would gradually transform Korea into a homogeneous society and ultimately establish a unified democracy.

North Korea   South Korea

South-North Coalition

Homogeneous Society

Unification

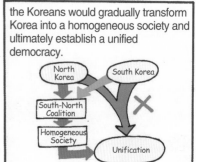

What is important here is that the South-North Coalition is not a coalition between the South and North Korean governments.

It is a special relationship that transcends such dimensions.

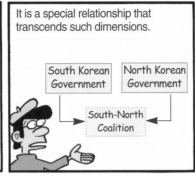

Under this arrangement, the South and North Korean governments would, for the time being, maintain their sovereignty.

Through the South-North Coalition, the two Koreas would start to promote economic and cultural exchanges and cooperation.

It would be a transitory stage during which

the groundwork for a unified nation would be laid.

Starting with summit meetings

and inter-Korean ministerial meetings,

which would lead to the establishment of a council consisting of representatives from South and North Korea,

the South-North Coalition would serve as the stepping stone to unification as well as its preparatory body.

Through the South-North Coalition, the Koreans would recover homogeneity as one people

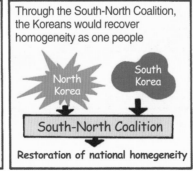

and eventually establish through peaceful means a unified government.

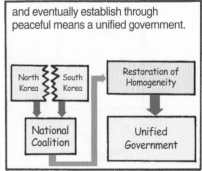

Well, that's the South Korean plan... Now, what's the Korean Federation Unification Plan proposed by North Korea?

Korean Federation

A federation is a nation consisting of two or more states.

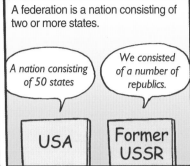

A nation consisting of 50 states

We consisted of a number of republics.

USA

Former USSR

The United States offers a good example.

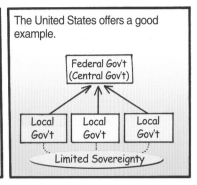

Federal Gov't (Central Gov't)

Local Gov't | Local Gov't | Local Gov't

Limited Sovereignty

The United States has a well developed federal system of government.

50 states constitute the United States.

California State Govt.

Texas State Govt.

Virginia State Govt.

⋮

Etc, Etc., 50 States

Each state is governed by its own government. The nation as a whole, however, is governed by the federal government.

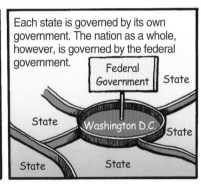

Federal Government | State

State

Washington D.C. | State

State | State

Each state government is autonomous to a certain extent, with the power to run its local affairs.

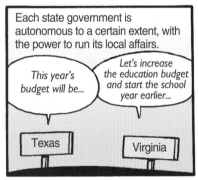

This year's budget will be...

Let's increase the education budget and start the school year earlier...

Texas | Virginia

The federal government is delegated with certain powers.

If each state had its own currency, its own army and its own interest rates,

there would arise massive disorder!

Federal Government

For example, California State and Gyeonggi Province* are free to establish trade relations with each other,

Let's exchange technologies.

Invest in our province!

California State-Gyeonggi Province Trade Agreement

* One of the provinces constituting the Republic of Korea

---

but the power to handle diplomatic relations at the national level is delegated to the federal government.

Peace on the Korean peninsula is very important to us.

The U.S. is behind you 100%.

The federal government is responsible for foreign affairs, national defense and national economic policy...

Foreign Affairs | Defense | Economy

Central Gov't

In a way, the federal government is superior to the 50 state governments.

Federal Government

State Government

The federal system espoused by North Korea resembles the U.S. and German federal systems.

Under this system, South and North Korea would maintain their individual sovereign governments

under a superior federal government,

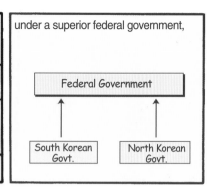

which would be delegated, for example, with the powers to handle foreign policy defense and national economic policy.

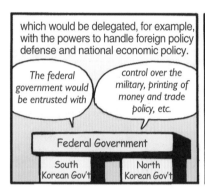

The difference between the federal system plan and the coalition plan is that,

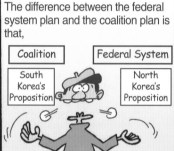

whereas the coalition plan promotes a gradual step-by-step unification process in order to first recover national homogeneity,

the federal system plan first calls for the creation of a unification government,

after which the issue of national homogeneity is to be considered.

Sounds like a great idea at first, right?

What's the big deal as long as each side recognizes the sovereignty of the other? After all, wouldn't this approach expedite the unification process?

The reason why South Korea cannot accept the federal system plan

is because of the three preconditions insisted upon by North Korea.

First condition. Withdraw the U.S. forces from South Korea.

Second condition. Repeal the National Security Law.

Third condition. Legalize the activities of the Communist Party in Korea.

You talk about unification without outside interference, but you maintain foreign military forces on the peninsula!

The U.S. is an imperialistic country just waiting to invade and take over North Korea!

Unification can never happen with the U.S. military on Korean soil!

And what about the National Security Law? It punishes anyone coming into contact with, or speaking favorably of, North Korea.

With this kind of law in place, how are we even supposed to discuss unification?

Only when you repeal this law, will North and South Koreans be able to meet and discuss the possibilities of a peaceful unification!

Legalize the Communist Party! How's reunification supposed to happen when the South Koreans implement such drastic anti-communist policies!

And, of course... if a free, democratic and unified Korea is born, the people must enjoy ideological freedom.

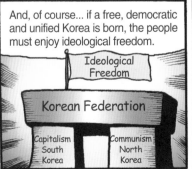

How would the freedom to engage in political activities be guaranteed if the Communist Party continues to be outlawed?

Well, sounds like you got some good points there. | But careful consideration proves otherwise!

The South Koreans can never accept these preconditions because there's a carefully planned ulterior motive behind all of this!

I'll tell you the reason why we can't accept these three preconditions.

· Withdrawal of U.S. Military
· Repeal of National Security Law
· Legalization of Communist Party

First, the withdrawal of the U.S. military.

Good-bye! Korea!

Korean peninsula

U.S. ARMY

U.S. soldiers have been stationed in Korea ever since the Korean War. Currently, there are about 37,000 U.S. soldiers stationed in South Korea.

To be sure, it is not the most pleasant of situations for the South Koreans to have a foreign military presence on their soil.

We have to provide land

U.S. ARMY

and pay for their expenses

But reality dictates otherwise. Technically, the two Koreas are still at war with only a ceasefire agreement in place.

This is a stupid piece of paper.

Ceasefire Agreement

Morever, North Korea maintains a much larger military force than South Korea.

Regular forces
1,170,000 soldiers
Reserve forces
7,500,000 soldiers

From the perspective of sheer size, the South Korean military is no match for the North Korean military.

The continued presence of the U.S. military in Korea is attributable to Korea's strategic geographical location.

Military Alliance

But, of course, more importantly, the U.S. military serves as a deterrent to an invasion by North Korea.

bang

South Korea

Any such invasion would bring North Korea face to face with the most powerful nation in the world.

Allied Forces

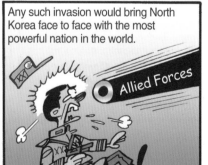

Thus, despite its overwhelming military might, North Korea has not been able to 'swallow' South Korea

due to the presence of the U.S. military in South Korea.

Oh, that little

If the U.S. military were to withdraw from South Korea,

this would break the balance of power on the Korean peninsula.

he he he

With only a ceasefire agreement in place,

Nobody will get in the way anymore, right!

there would be no other mechanism that would deter an invasion by North Korea.

crack

The same logic applies to North Korea's demand to repeal the National Security Law.

It's an obstacle to unification!

National Security Law

The National Security Law was enacted in order to promote national security and to restrict antigovernment activities.

Overthrow the government!

National Security Law
Law No. 3318
1980. 12. 31.

Unification through communization!

This statute replaced the previous version of the National Security Law and the Anti-Communism Law.

National Security Law
Law No. 549
1963. 6. 10.

폐지! *

Anti-Communism Law
Law No. 643
1961. 7. 3.

* Repealed

The National Security Law prescribes certain organizations as anti-state organizations and strictly restricts their activities.

National Security Law

An anti-state organization refers to an organization that was formed for subversive purposes or

The incumbent government needs to hit the road!

Until then, we're in charge! We'll overthrow this government and start a new era!

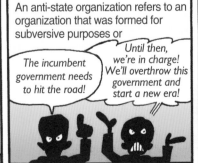

to adhere to communist-related lines of activities with such purposes.

XX Democratic Youths

XX Unification Society

Workers' Revolution XX

People's Revolutionary XX

Revolutionaries of XX

The National Security Law was enacted in 1980 by the new military regime that staged a coup d'etat on December 12, 1979*.

Freeze!

bang bang

Or else!

* See page 142.

Its purpose was to preserve the security of the new regime

Ra ra

What's all the racket about??

by persecuting opposition forces as anti-state organizations.

National Security Law

Democracy!

The National Security Law enabled the government to accuse anyone of engaging in anti-state activities.

You commie sympathizer!

Many people cried out for its outright repeal.

Abolish the National Security Law!

However, to a certain extent, the National Security Law does serve as a device to preserve national security.

National Security Law

State

Its outright repeal would result in the disarmament of Korean society.

Now, I can freely go to North Korea!

Yippee! All hail the Dear Leader, Kim Jong Il!

True, there is a need to substantially amend the statute,

The voice of the conscience!

National Security Law

NO!

but its outright repeal may result in the infiltration of harmful elements from North Korea.

Let's fire up those anti-American sentiments!

Let's stomp out the American imperialists in the name of the people!

In such case, there is a great risk that South Korean society would be overwhelmed by disorder and conflict.

That's why it's impossible to accept the North Korean demands.

Scrapping the National Security Law without offering a better alternative will not do!

Nat'l Security Law

What about the condition that South Korea permit the activities of the Communist Party?

That's old school! Try this!

Legalization of Communist Party

Anti-Communism

North Korea is a strictly controlled society.

Compared to the North Koreans who have been brainwashed to blindly accept the communist ideology,

the South Koreans are accustomed to the free exchange of ideas and opinions, the bedrock principles of a democratic society.

If communism were to be permitted in South Korea,

forces backed by North Korea may agitate student groups and labor unions,

among others, thereby wreaking havoc on South Korean society.

Of course, if North Korea were to open its doors and embrace democracy,

and guarantee basic rights,

there would be no reason to oppose the Communist Party.

North Korea's one-sided demands, however,

are the product of its ulterior motives.

That is, North Korea continues to insist on its federal system unification plan due to its desire to achieve unification through communization.

So far, we have looked at the proposed plans for unification of South and North Korea.

If both sides truly wish to unify the Korean peninsula,

it goes without saying that there should be room for compromise between the two sides.

But if North Korea adamantly adheres to its position to communize South Korea,

the Korean peninsula could remain divided indefinitely.

Thus, any progress can be made only if North Korea drops this position.

In fact, it is doubtful as to whether North Korea truly believes it could realize the communization of South Korea.

This is so because, except for its well-oiled military machine,

North Korea, especially its economy, is literally sinking.

In contrast, South Korea is now ranked as the 13th largest economy in the world with a per capita GNI of US$10,000.

The sheer difference in the sizes of the two economies is a factor that discourages North Korea from acting on its professed goal.

Of course, North Korea is also aware that South Korea would not sit by idly if there are any attempts to forcefully unify the Korean peninsula.

If this is the case, why wouldn't North Korea just drop such a drastic policy line?

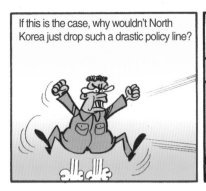

We should take into account that the North Korean regime maintains a large armed forces numbering over 1 million.

As the Defense Chairman, I'm the supreme leader!

All Hail the Dear Leader!

The justification for maintaining such a large military is the 'liberation' of South Korea.

Liberation of South Korea!

Communist Unification!

If North Korea were to renounce its policy line to 'liberate' South Korea, it would be forsaking the very foundation on which its regime is built.

Renunciation of Policy Line	→	Renunciation of War	→	No Justification for Maintaining Large Armed Forces

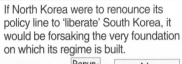

Needless to say, powerful military leaders would vehemently oppose any such development.

If there's going to be no war, what are we doing here?

We're all gonna be jobless. I can just tell!

So, the North Korean regime would risk undergoing a collapse.

Military   Circles

In other words, the suvival of the North Korean regime for over 50 years

North Korean Government 1945-Present

was based on this foundation.

Until the day of unification,

...Let's follow the Great Leader and overcome all hardships!

This is why North Korea continues to profess a desire to achieve unification through communization even though the times have changed.

communization

Why don't you sing to another tune?

The times have indeed changed. The Eastern European Bloc and, in fact, most communist countries have disappeared.

crumble

Communist regimes

Europe

Germany has unified. But it was communist East Germany that was merged into West Germany.

This, of course, was a tremendous shock to North Korea.

D

DDR

North Korea... the only hardline Stalinist state left in the world...

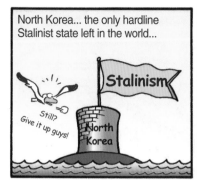

Even their most trusted ally, China, has turned to capitalism...

Undoubtedly, this has made North Korea very uneasy.

North Korea may be tempted to go the path of an all-out war with South Korea,

But it does not stand a chance against the combined South Korean-U.S. forces.

If a war broke out, North Korea's very foundation would be turned upside down.

North Korea is not foolish enough to risk losing everything like that.

But the North Korean dilemma is that it is also not in a position to pursue Chinese-style reforms.

Such reforms would remove barriers to information on the outside world

and provoke the North Korean people who were deceived for decades about the truth of their situation.

Thus, the opening up of North Korea and the implementation of reforms are likely to lead to the fall of the North Korean regime.

Against such a backdrop, it is obvious what the North Korean regime has in mind.

Given that the 'liberation' of South Korea is now a farfetched dream,

and that its economy is on the verge of collapse, North Korea has no alternative but to open its doors and implement reforms.

That would lead to the collapse of the regime! We would be absorbed by South Korea!

The more they come into contact with South Korea, the more the North Koreans would realize how affluent the South Koreans are.

Obviously, this would put the North Korean regime in a precarious position.

Reunion of separated families? Prevent it from happening!

Summit talks? Use any excuse to avoid it!

North Korea's ulterior motive is to cut off ties with South Korea in order to safeguard the stability of its regime.

Nevertheless, in order to rebuild its floundering economy, North Korea badly needs cash from South Korea.

So its strategy is to squeeze as much money as it can from South Korea

but to minimize contact in order to prevent the opening of North Korea.

If that is the case, then how do the South Koreans themselves view the issue of the unification of Korea?

Unification

Of course, a large majority of the South Koreans voice their strong desire for unification.

It is at the top of their wish list.

There's no 21st century without unification!

The future of our people depends on unification!

It's the most pressing issue!

But there is a significant minority who fear the enormous burden that unification would entail.

Well, unification is important but...

If unification suddenly occurred, would we realistically have the capacity to deal with it?

The Koreans, who have yearned for the unification of Korea,

Whatever it takes...

We must unite...

I mean now!

came to realize that everything was not rosy with unification through another incident.

Wow! Can you believe that?!

It was the German unification. The Koreans learned a valuable lesson from the German experience.

Unification

West Germany

East Germany

It was that South Korea should not absorb North Korea as West Germany absorbed East Germany.

That's not the

way to do it!

As former German Chancellor Helmut Kohl confessed, the German unification happened so unexpectedly.

I myself didn't expect the unification of Germany to happen so quickly.

Although the German unification was a product of the strong desire of the East Germans,

So sick and tired of socialism!

We want the freedom and wealth enjoyed by our brothers and sisters in the West!

the burden of reconstructing East Germany fell entirely on the West Germans.

Unification

Costs of Unification

At that time, West Germany was the most affluent nation in Western Europe,

whereas East Germany was the most affluent nation in Eastern Europe.

Highest per capita GNI among socialist countries

Nevertheless, there was a very large disparity between the income of West Germans and East Germans (by as much as 10-fold).

West Germany

East Germany

$30,000 $3,000

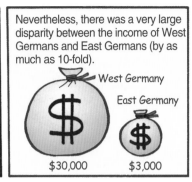

After unification, West Germany poured astronomical sums of money into the reconstruction of East Germany.

gluck
gluck

This has been going on for more than 10 years.

No end in sight!

However, there still exists a large gap between the standards of living of the West and East Germans.

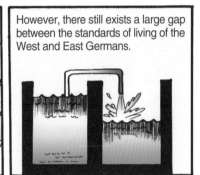

Thus, it is yet unknown how much more money will be required.

When will this end?

Of course, the costs of unification come from taxpayers' money.

Unif. Costs

tax

tax

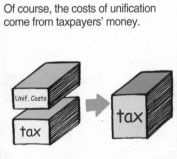

The West Germans have been patient about the tax increases, but there is some concern.

What can we do... They're Germans too...

We'd have to pay for it one way or the other...

If West Germany's economy had not been strong enough

grrr

to sustain such a burden,

Unification Costs

both West and East Germany would have collapsed under the weight of the enormous costs of unification.

crash

Sorry for having you shoulder everything.

Unification Costs

What would happen if the Korean peninsula was suddenly unified? Obviousy, South Korea would have to bear the burden of unification.

Unification costs

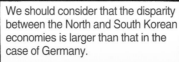

We should consider that the disparity between the North and South Korean economies is larger than that in the case of Germany.

South Korea

North Korea

$

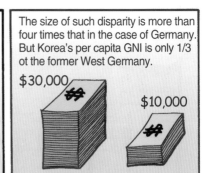

The size of such disparity is more than four times that in the case of Germany. But Korea's per capita GNI is only 1/3 ot the former West Germany.

$30,000

$10,000

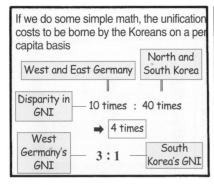

If we do some simple math, the unification costs to be borne by the Koreans on a per capita basis

West and East Germany	North and South Korea
Disparity in GNI	10 times : 40 times
	➡ 4 times
West Germany's GNI	3 : 1	South Korea's GNI

is more than 12 times the unification costs borne by the Germans on a per capita basis.

South Korean Burden

West German Burden

Of course, this would be an unrealistic burden for South Korea.

This would lead to

the collapse of both Koreas!

Unification

No matter how important unification is to us,

how many of us would want to go to such extremes?

Even without considering unification, I'm breaking my back here paying for my kid's education!

What would happen if the taxes were raised manyfold?

East Germany was the most affluent communist country when it was absorbed into West Germany, whereas North Korea is now one of the poorest countries in the world.

The costs of reconstructing North Korea would be staggering–nothing like the German experience in terms of the magnitude.

Impossible!

In fact, the lesson learned from the German experience was to not approach unification in such a fashion.

You're opposing unification just because of the economics? You traitor!

You're full of it! I need to feed my family first!

Aside from the economic problem, another serious problem is the widening gap between the two Korean societies.

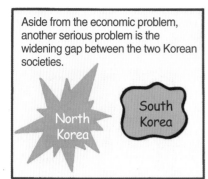

For a period of over 50 years after the liberation from Japan,

the South and North Koreans have been completely segregated from each other.

Ceasefire Line

Brother...

I miss my brother in the North...

More than five decades have passed without any exchanges whatsoever... 50 years is a long time.

Pyongyang | Seoul

The Koreans are one people in name only. They are no different than people from two different nations.

Corner kick from comrade Kim!

Kim Jeong-chul makes the corner kick!

Their ways of thinking and life styles

Sharing the fruits of labor and cooperation! Responsibility of the state!

Equal opportunity and competition! Responsibility for oneself!

and languages have drifted apart.

My female comrade, do you like dog meat?

Oh my goodness! No! I like spaghetti or pizza.

If unification does occur in the future,

Brother!

Brother!

it is questionable whether the two sides would be able to communicate with each other with ease.

Are you saying this interest thing gives birth to money? Does money bear babies, too, in South Korea??

Uhhh... You see... That's a fundamental principle of capitalism... Whew...

This is likely to lead to conflict and dispute between the two sides.

Comrade president, take a good look at yourself!

There may be great social upheavals in the unified Korea.

It is only natural that many South Korean are apprehensive of the consequences of a sudden unification.

Needless to say, there is also the ideological difference between the South and North Koreans.

Even though North Korea is an extremely poor country, as residents of a socialist state, its people believe that they live in an egalitarian society.

Comrade! Comrade! Comrade!

Even though they are equal only in their poverty, egalitarianism is deeply embedded in the minds of the North Koreans.

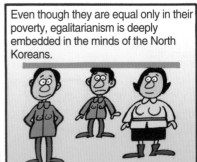

Thus, it would be difficult for them to accept the gap between the rich and the poor and their low status in unified Korean society.

If North Korea adopts capitalism after unification,

North

Capitalism

it is likely that the North Koreans would have no alternative but to work for South Korean capitalists.

Work hard or you will get the axe!

There would be discontent over the inequalities characterizing the new society.

The socialist constitution provides that the unemployed must be provided with jobs!

How could a company dismiss its workers! We're only accountable to the party!

If such discontent leads to organized activities,

Let's overthrow the South Korean capitalists!

All North Korean workers unite!

Raa raa

Return to socialism!

Restore the ideology of self-reliance!

the Korean peninsula would be engulfed by chaos.

Bang

Bang

Unified Korea

Both sides worry about this possibility...

It's something we'll have to go through at some point...

Although both South and North Korea voice their desire for unification, reality dictates that each side tread cautiously as it seeks to achieve this goal.

We wish for and dream of unification~

Don't come near us! Stay away! Leave us alone!

We must tread carefully and not rush the process...

However, sooner or later, the two Koreas will have to deal with the problem of unification in earnest.

Out of fear that its regime may collapse, North Korea avoids any interaction with South Korea.

It is possible that North Korea may resort to extreme means to overcome its current predicament.

For this reason, the threat of war continues to exist on the Korean peninsula.

The problem is that, although the North Korean economy is on the brink of bankruptcy,

North Korea continues to distrust South Korea.

In this regard, South Korea has adopted an engagement policy

to bring North Korea to the negotiation table in order to gain its trust and avoid the risk of war.

It is a policy of tolerance and cooperation to grow together through economic and cultural exchanges.

This is the so-called Sunshine Policy.

There appears to be no other alternative today but for South Korea to pursue such an engagement policy.

If the Sunshine Policy ever becomes tainted by

Distrust Antagonism

It's warm today. Maybe I'll take off my coat today.

an ulterior motive, it is likely to backfire.

Still not going to take off that coat?

It would just make North Korea more suspicious and wary.

Turning up the heat so I'll take off my coat, huh?

North Korea would become even more distrustful.

I may fry to death but I ain't taking it off! Never!

Thus, the Sunshine Policy must be based on a brotherly love towards North Korea,

He needs warm sunlight to relieve himself from the cold.

an unconditional love towards the Korean brethren.

Yippee! I think I'm gonna make it!

This must continue on until the day of unification.

In other words, the essence of the Sunshine Policy is not materialistic but attitudinal.

I don't think of you as an enemy... You're my brother!

The goal is to coexist and prosper together and to avoid war!

Although the North Korean regime is in desperate need of economic aid from South Korea,

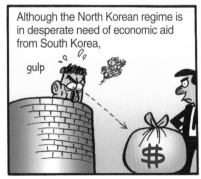

gulp

its basic policy is to avoid any interaction that may pose a threat to the regime,

Yeah we need the South Koreans' help... but I ain't opening these doors.

and to procure as much aid as possible.

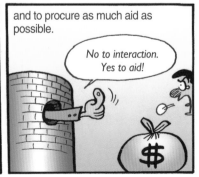

No to interaction. Yes to aid!

However, a one-sided engagement policy

will not achieve much.

Instead, it would only 'spoil' North Korea.

The Sunshine Policy is modeled after the Ospolitik of former West German Chancellor Willy Brandt.

In 1970, West and East Germany signed a treaty

that liberalized West German travel to East Germany.

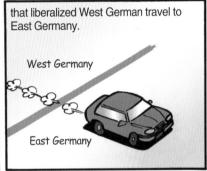

In exchange, West Germany provided a significant economic aid package to East Germany.

However, the West Germans did not politically take advantage of this new development.

But at the same time, West Germany did not blindly confer aid on East Germany.

They ensured that the benefit of economic aid was shared by the people of both West and East Germany.

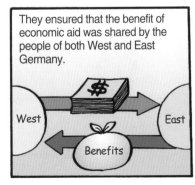

This is how they built the foundation for German unification.

This, in fact, is what should be the model for the Sunshine Policy of Korea.

233

Faced by crises on all sides, North Korea has become more sensitive than ever before.

For the time being, it would be difficult for North Korea to open up and implement reforms.

> Reform = Collapse of regime

> We saw what happened to the Soviet Union after they opened their doors and made reforms!

In other words, realistically, it is yet premature for unification to occur on the Korean peninsula.

> That door needs to open before we can move forward.

Although South Korea must continue its engagement policy towards North Korea,

it is important to not provoke the sensitive North Korean regime.

> Come out and play!

> Let's negotiate!

> Let's host an event together!

> I said no! Why do you keep bothering us?

Unification must be pursued on a systematic step-by-step basis.

> Skipping a step means drowning!

The South Koreans should look at the reality confronting the Korean peninsula with a cool head.

Instead of blindly pursuing unification,

> It's dangerous if we go too fast!

> Anti-unificationist!

exchanges on economic, academic and artistic levels must first be implemented.

> We must start with things that won't shake the very foundation of the regime.

Efforts to study how far the two Koreas have culturally and socially drifted apart should be made

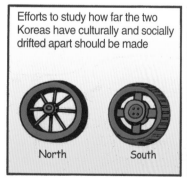

North   South

in order to reduce the gap between the two Koreas,

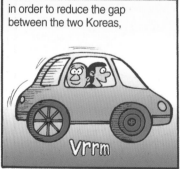

Vrrm

as, one day, they will indeed become unified!

* Unification

abolish VERB

If someone in authority abolishes a system or practice, he formally puts an end to it.

EX When the government abolished the entrance exam and switched to a lottery system, the former students who had taken the entrance exam didn't acknowledge the 'lottery' students as fellow alumni. (74)

absolutely ADV

Absolutely means totally and completely.

EX We have absolutely no luck when it comes to leaders! (104)

abuse VERB

If you abuse something, you use it in a wrong way or for a bad purpose.

EX They abuse political connections and offer bribes for special interest. (160)

accomplishment N-COUNT

An accomplishment is something remarkable that has been done or achieved.

EX Many Koreans today still revere and respect Park Chung Hee and his accomplishments. (140)

accumulate VERB

When you accumulate things or when they accumulate, they collect or are gathered over a period of time.

EX Only then would one have accumulated sufficient direct and indirect experience that fuels creativity. (172)

adaptation N-COUNT

When you adapt something, you adjust or change it to become suitable to a new or special application or situation.

EX The successful adaptation of these two models to fit the Korean situation was the key to Korea's success. (188)

adhere VERB

If you adhere to a rule or agreement, you act in the way that it says you should.

EX They adhered to an orthodoxy that embraced only the fundamental. (59)

affluent ADJ

If you are affluent, you have a lot of money.

EX Of course, the younger generation that grew up during more affluent and comfortable times have a hard time blindly sympathizing this 'hungry spirit.' (159)

alternative N-COUNT

If one thing is an alternative to another, the first can be found, used, or done instead of the second.

EX Although you can't smell fresh soil, apartments would be the only alternative. (63)

analogy N-COUNT

If you make or draw an analogy between two things, you show that they are similar in some way.

EX In Tokyo's case, during the peak of the bubble economy in 1989, an interesting analogy was used to describe Tokyo's land prices. (184)

appointment N-VAR

The appointment of a person to a particular job is the choice of that person to do it.

EX There was endless criticism over the appointment of persons from his hometown to major government posts. (180)

apprentice N-COUNT

An apprentice is a young person who works for someone in order to learn his skill.

EX In agricultural societies, knowledge or secrets of the trade are passed on to younger generations through an apprentice system. (172)

arise from VERB

If something arises from a particular situation,

or arises out of it, it is created or caused by the situation.

EX It is a temperament that arose from the special circumstances of peninsular countries. (60)

ascend VERB
If you ascend a hill or staircase, you go up it.

EX Although the Japanese court also stressed tradition, the most qualified person usually ascended to the throne. (73)

aspire VERB
If you aspire to something such as an important job, you have a strong desire to achieve it.

EX As long as each Korean aspires to live by this seonbi spirit, Korea can overcome any obstacle confronting the country. (55)

assimilate VERB
When people such as immigrants assimilate into a community or when that community assimilates them, they become an accepted part of it.

EX Most of the Japanese have assimilated into American society, so it's difficult to find large-scale Japan towns in America. (149)

at all costs PHRASE
If you say that something must be avoided at all costs, you are emphasizing that it must not be allowed to happen under any circumstances.

EX The relentless pursuit of the anachronistic goal to enter prestigious universities at all costs has paradoxically resulted in enormous money and efforts being invested by parents to only cause the deterioration of the competitiveness of their children. (174)

at stake PHRASE
If something is at stake, it is being risked and might be lost or damaged if you are not successful.

EX Korean parents put everything at stake for their children's education. (165)

authentic ADJ
An authentic person, object, or emotion is genuine.

EX What does it mean to be 'authentic?' Nothing must have been added or changed. In other words, the original purity must not have been impaired. (70)

authoritarian ADJ
If you describe a person or an organization as authoritarian, you are critical of them controlling everything rather than letting people decide things for themselves.

EX However, there is no doubt that, under Park's authoritarian rule, Korea's economy grew by leaps and bounds. (176)

bankrupt ADJ
People or organizations that go bankrupt do not have enough money to pay their debts.

EX The problem is that, although the North Korean economy is on the brink of bankruptcy, North Korea continues to distrust South Korea. (231)

blow up PHRASE VERB
If someone blows something up or if it blows up, it is destroyed by an explosion.

EX However, the Korean government blew up a bridge crossing the Han River to slow down the North Korean army's march towards the south. (124)

bound to PHRASE
If you say that something is bound to happen, you mean that you are sure it will happen, because it is a natural consequence of something that is already known or exists.

EX Go to any place in America; there are bound to be some Koreans around! (148)

boundary N-COUNT

The boundary of an area of land is an imaginary line that separates it from other areas.

EX Although only goods and money have been able to move across boundaries so far, in the near future, workers and services will be able to do so as well. (170)

bribe VERB

A bribe is a sum of money or something valuable that one person offers or gives to another in order to persuade him or her to do something.

EX You're trying to bribe me! Take it back! (54)

brutal ADJ

A brutal act or person is cruel and violent.

EX The result would've been endless brutal wars without boundaries or limits. (27)

budget N-COUNT

Your budget is the amount of money that you have available to spend. The budget for something is the amount of money that a person, organization, or country has available to spend on it.

EX This is equal to about 31.4% of the government's 22.7 trillion won budget for education. (168)

capable ADJ

If a person or thing is capable of doing something, they have the ability to do it.

EX Only a capable person with vision and exceptional leadership can guide the people of a nation. (175)

carry on PHRASE VERB

If you carry on doing something, you continue to do it.

EX Trust the government and carry on with your daily work. (124)

classify VERB

To classify things means to divide them into groups or types so that things with similar characteristics are in the same group.

EX The World Bank classifies these countries into three major groups. (11)

cling to VERB

If you cling to someone or something, you hold onto them tightly.

EX Although nearly all the communist countries have fallen, the North Koreans still cling to the most extreme form of Stalinism. (93)

coalition N-COUNT

A coalition is a government consisting of people from two or more political parties.

EX The crux of the Korean Community Unification Plan is the formation of a transitory coalition between South and North Korea. (212)

coin VERB

If you coin a word or a phrase, you are the first person to say it.

EX Pariah capitalism is a term coined by German sociologist and political economist, Max Weber. (161)

collective ADJ

Collective actions, situations, or feelings involve or are shared by every member of a group of people.

EX The explosive economic growth during the 1960s was a result of the collective effort of the Korean people. (296)

collision N-VAR

A collision occurs when a moving object crashes into something.

EX It's the collision of the vertical social structure and the horizontal way of thinking. (104)

come across PHRASE VERB
If you come across something or someone, you find them or meet them by chance.
EX While reading this book, you will come across certain phrases like 'the world's greatest' or 'the world's best.' (10)

compromise N-VAR
A compromise is a situation in which people accept something slightly different from what they really want, because of circumstances or because they are considering the wishes of other people.
EX Due to their obsession to avoid defeat, instead of engaging in dialogue or attempting to compromise, the Koreans tend to settle things by force. (132)

conflict N-COUNT
Conflict is serious disagreement and argument about something important. If two people or groups are in conflict, they have had a serious disagreement or argument and have not yet reached agreement.
EX Let's consider as an example the conflict between the pharmacists and the oriental medicine doctors in Korea. (133)

consciousness N-COUNT
Your consciousness is your mind and your thoughts.
EX A national consciousness of unity developed as the Koreans came together to fend off foreign aggressors. (22)

consequence N-COUNT
The consequences of something are the results or effects of it.
EX You should be prepared to suffer the negative consequences. (131)

consider VERB
If you consider a person or thing to be something, you have the opinion that this is

what they are.
EX People without genealogical lines are considered 'rootless' families. (71)

cooperative ADJ
A co-operative activity is done by people working together.
EX In other words, it was a village-unit cooperative work organization. (126)

cozy ADJ
A house or room that is cozy is comfortable and warm.
EX With limited space, if everybody wanted to live in a warm cozy home... What would it take? (63)

crave VERB
If you crave something, you want to have it very much.
EX It's not the craving for Korean food that drives them to Korean restaurants. (86)

cronyism N-COUNT
If you accuse someone in authority of cronyism, you mean that they use their power or authority to get jobs for their friends.
EX All of this exemplifies the deeply rooted cronyism in Korean society. (83)

decent ADJ
Decent is used to describe something which is considered to be of an acceptable standard or quality.
EX If a country does not develop its industries and create jobs for the people, only a few crafty people will make a decent living. (157)

declare VERB
If you declare that something is true, you say that it is true in a firm, deliberate way. You can also declare an attitude or intention.

EX Before Christianity could spread into China, the socialist government declared that religion was a mere opium of the people. (89)

delegate VERB
If you delegate duties, responsibilities, or power to someone, you give them those duties, those responsibilities, or that power so that they can act on your behalf.

EX The federal government is delegated with certain powers. (215)

delicate ADJ
Something that is delicate is small and beautifully shaped.

EX If this delicate balance is broken, a rift develops in the friendship. (80)

deprive of VERB
If you deprive someone of something that they want or need, you take it away from them, or you prevent them from having it.

EX Hence, the 20th century started with Korea being deprived of its sovereignty. (135)

derive from VERB
If you derive something such as pleasure or benefit from a person or from something, you get it from them.

EX 70% of the Korean language is derived from Chinese words but only one pronunciation is recognized for each character. (78)

desperate ADJ
If you are desperate, you are in such a bad situation that you are willing to try anything to change it.

EX Although the North Korean regime is in desperate need of economic aid from South Korea··· (232)

despise VERB
If you despise something or someone, you dislike them and have a very low opinion of them.

EX The Europeans generally despised the Jews. (162)

devastate VERB
If something devastates another person or thing, it damages or totally destroys that person or thing.

EX The people were profoundly devastated, living in fear for their lives and suffering from poverty. (24)

dictatorship N-VAR
Dictatorship is government by a dictator. A dictator is a person who tells people what they should do or can do.

EX In the meantime, of course, those who fought against his dictatorship for democracy are never to be forgotten. (178)

differ V-RECIP
If two or more things differ, they are unlike each other in some way.

EX These countries greatly differ from one another. (22)

diploma N-COUNT
A diploma is a qualification which may be awarded to a student by a university or college, or by a high school in the United States.

EX I made it! I got my diploma! (166)

diplomatic ADJ
Diplomatic means relating to diplomacy and diplomats.

EX In 1905, Japan stripped Joseon of its diplomatic power through a protectorate treaty. (135)

discard VERB
If you discard something, you get rid of it because you no longer want it or need it.

EX In order for such a leader to emerge, the cynicism and distrust prevailing in Korean society must be discarded. (203)

discriminate VERB

To discriminate against a group of people or in favor of a group of people means to unfairly treat them worse or better than other groups.

EX He was discriminated against in the cruelest ways, forbidden to even utter the word 'father.' (73)

disguise VERB

To disguise something means to hide it or make it appear different so that people will not know about it or will not recognize it.

EX But it started popping up disguised in the name of 'equality' and 'justice.' (143)

disorder N-COUNT

Disorder is a state of being untidy, badly prepared, or badly organized.

EX As a matter of course, there would be unimaginable disorder and chaos if the two Koreas are unified overnight. (212)

dispute N-VAR

A dispute is an argument or disagreement between people or groups.

EX This leads to endless disputes between communities. (132)

distinction N-COUNT

A distinction between similar things is a difference.

EX Why do we make this distinction? (12)

drain VERB

If you drain something from a place or object, you remove it by causing it to flow somewhere else. If something drains somewhere, it flows there.

EX The people end up suffering the most, while the national wealth is drained. (121)

due to PREP-PHRASE

You can say 'due to' to introduce the reason for something happening. Some speakers of English believe that it is not correct to use 'due to' in this way.

EX However, due to the impact of the Asian financial crisis in 1997, which caused the value of the US Dollar to sharply appreciate against the Korean Won, Korea's per capita GNI dropped to US $8,490 (11)

dye VERB

If you dye something such as hair or cloth, you change its color by soaking it in a special liquid.

EX As late as in the mid 1990s, Korean people thought it was very strange for youths to dye their hair. (69)

egalitarian ADJ

Egalitarian means supporting or following the idea that all people are equal and should have the same rights and opportunities.

EX The hierarchical power structure of Park's era has weakened, whereas, after long and endless struggles for democracy, the horizontal egalitarian way of thinking has grown much stronger. (178)

embedded VERB

If something such as an attitude or feeling is embedded in a society or system, or in someone's personality, that thing becomes a permanent and noticeable feature of the society or system.

EX Why do so many Koreans visit their home-towns during the holiday seasons? It's a concept embedded and ingrained in their thoughts. (68)

engage in VERB

If you engage in an activity, you do it or are actively involved with it.

EX But this isn't quite that easy for the Koreans, as they engage in a sign warfare, battling as if their lives depend on it. (64)

engulf VERB
If one thing engulfs another, it completely covers or hides it, often in a sudden and unexpected way.
EX During this period, after the army gained control of the government, Japan became engulfed by militarism. (109)

erupt VERB
When something erupts, it bursts forth or out, as from some restraint.
EX The French Revolution erupted in 1789. (100)

ethnic ADJ
Ethnic means connected with or relating to different racial or cultural groups of people.
EX Different ethnic people were constantly at war in continental and peninsular countries. (33)

eventually ADV
Eventually means in the end, especially after a lot of delays, problems, or arguments.
EX And, eventually, they started a war against the United States and its allies. (109)

evidently ADV
You use evidently to say that something is obviously true, for example, because you have seen evidence of it yourself.
EX Evidently, the younger generation lacks the 'hungry spirit' of their parents. (159)

exaggerate VERB
If you exaggerate, you indicate that something is, for example, worse or more important than it really is.
EX Would it be an exaggeration to say that everything is extreme and drastic in Korea? (84)

examine VERB
If you examine something, you look at it carefully.

EX Let's examine the unification issue and see why there lies ahead such a treacherous road. (208)

exclude VERB
If you exclude someone or something from a place or activity or from consideration, you prevent that person or thing from entering it or taking part in it or being considered for it.
EX Excluded from the scope of our comparison are those countries with the majority of their people suffering from poverty. (12)

exemplify VERB
If a person or thing exemplifies something such as a situation, quality, or class of things, that person or thing serves as a typical example.
EX The fact that the Koreans value authenticity and legitimacy is also exemplified by their attitude towards genealogy. (70)

exhaust VERB
If you are exhausted, you are so tired, either physically or mentally, that you have no energy left.
EX After working day and night, and becoming fatigued and exhausted, listening to the words of God gave them strength and comfort. (92)

exploit VERB
If you say that someone is exploiting you, you think that they are treating you unfairly by using your work or ideas and giving you very little in return.
EX On the other hand, the Koreans greatly suffered from the exploitation of the Japanese. (108)

extracurricular VERB
Extracurricular activities are activities for students that are not part of their main course of study.
EX To survive this 'war,' the demand for extracurricular studies skyrocketed. (115)

flee VERB

If you flee from something or someone, or flee a person or thing, you escape and run away from them.

EX The Joseon royal family fled to Ganghwado and then Namhansansung. (123)

frugal ADJ

People who are frugal or who live frugal lives do not eat much or spend much money on themselves.

EX But most Koreans are industrious and frugal people who won't go near luxury items. (158)

fundamental ADJ

You use fundamental to describe things, activities, and principles that are very important or essential. They affect the basic nature of other things or are the most important element upon which other things depend.

EX During the 1970s and 1980s, education became the fundamental stepping stone to success. (166)

glimpse N-COUNT

If you get a glimpse of someone or something, you see them very briefly and not very well.

EX What did Napoleon have to say after catching a glimpse of China's potential? (30)

greasy ADJ

Something that is greasy has grease on it or in it.

EX Take a look at this bland and greasy food! (86)

green card N-COUNT

A green card is the informal name of a document showing that someone who is not a citizen of the United States has permission to live and work there.

EX I'm going to get my green card and live here! (174)

hierarchy N-VAR

A hierarchy is a system of organizing people into different ranks or levels of importance, for example in society or in a company.

EX Due to Confucian traditions, it is important to be aware of hierarchy and rank in Korean society. (79)

homogeneous ADJ

Homogeneous is used to describe a group or thing which has members or parts that are all the same.

EX Regardless of the size of their population, they are each a homogeneous people. (22)

horizontal ADJ

Something that is horizontal is flat and level with the ground, rather than at an angle to it. Horizontal also refers to something of or pertaining to a position or individual of similar status.

EX It is the cooperation within a community based on horizontal relationships, a community with common goals and interests. (195)

hypocrisy N-VAR

If you accuse someone of hypocrisy, you mean that they pretend to have qualities, beliefs, or feelings that they do not really have.

EX Hypocrisy and distrust prevailed throughout society during this period. (141)

ideology N-VAR

An ideology is a set of beliefs, especially the political beliefs on which people, parties, or countries base their actions.

EX Well, just how extreme are the ideologies of the Koreans? (93)

ignorant ADJ

If you describe someone as ignorant, you mean that they do not know things they should know. If someone is ignorant of a fact, they do not know it.

EX If one is ignorant of these terms in Korea, he's headed for trouble. (80)

imitate VERB

If you imitate someone, you copy what they do or produce.

EX Thus, the Koreans can no longer simply imitate the American and Japanese models. (193)

immediately ADV

If something happens immediately, it happens without any delay.

EX Given that the Koreans cannot stand falling behind others, anything different immediately catches the eyes of neighbors. (63)

imperative ADJ

If it is imperative that something is done, that thing is extremely important and absolutely required and unavoidable.

EX Moving ahead or falling behind would disrupt the egalitarian relationship that is imperative in Korean society. (128)

imperialism N-COUNT

Imperialism is a system in which a rich and powerful country controls other countries, or a desire for control over other countries.

EX It was a period during which imperialism prevailed. (135)

implication N-COUNT

The implications of something are the things that are implied or suggested as naturally to be inferred or understood.

EX This also had implications for the security of the U.S. (137)

impose VERB

If you impose something on people, you use your authority to force them to accept it.

EX Nevertheless, the complexities of society demand that order and rules be imposed on economic activities. (160)

impoverish VERB

Something that impoverishes a person or a country makes them poor.

EX What do North Koreans think of this person who started the tragic Korean War and impoverished their nation? (182)

in essence PHRASE

You use 'in essence' to emphasize that you are talking about the most important or central aspect of an idea, situation, or event.

EX The Shogun was, in essence, the emperor, and, for that matter, the real person in charge. (35)

in no time PHRASE

If something happens in no time or in next to no time, it happens almost immediately or very quickly.

EX Undoubtedly, Korea will rejoin the ranks of high-income countries in no time. (11)

indicate VERB

If one thing indicates another, the first thing shows that the second is true or exists.

EX Basically, the exit polls indicated that the people had lied about their votes. (145)

inevitably ADV

If something will inevitably happen, it is certain to happen and cannot be prevented or avoided.

EX Inevitably, their personalities became very extreme. (45)

inherit VERB
If you inherit money or property, you receive it from someone who has died.

EX As long as there are the first and second sons, the third son cannot inherit the throne. (72)

innovation N-COUNT
An innovation is a new thing or a new method of doing something.

EX Thus, with a creative mind, it is important to assemble and combine various knowledge and information, from which innovations are created. (172)

inseparable ADJ
If one thing is inseparable from another, the things are so closely connected that they cannot be considered separately.

EX The economy and the land are inseparable! (192)

instability N-COUNT
Instability is the quality of being unstable.

EX Therefore, even advanced countries do experience a degree of instability in their politics. (99)

intensive ADJ
Intensive activity involves concentrating a lot of effort or people on one particular task in order to try to achieve a great deal in a short time.

EX They spend money abroad in countries like America, Australia and Canada, by sending their children to intensive foreign language programs during school vacations. (174)

intervention N-VAR
Intervention is the act of interfering in a situation.

EX Any decisions regarding the matter must be made by the Koreans themselves without the intervention of outside forces. (211)

investment N-UNCOUNT
Investment is the activity of putting something (money) to use to obtain a profit in return.

EX The problem is that despite the huge investments, the returns on such investments are very low, as exemplified by the low level of productivity. (169)

involvement N-UNCOUNT
Your involvement in something is the fact that you are taking part in it.

EX It's also a mystery to see parents end their involvement in their children's education once the college entrance exams are over. (173)

justification N-VAR
A justification for something is an acceptable reason or explanation for it.

EX 'Ordinary' justification was not enough. 'Noble' justification was required. (72)

lag behind VERB
If one thing or person lags behind another thing or person, their progress is slower than that of the other.

EX Irresponsible bureaucrats basked in unreasonable optimism, while the financial system lagged far behind global standards. (190)

loan N-COUNT
A loan is a sum of money that you borrow.

EX But, Korea has repaid the loans constituting the bailout package from the International Monetary Fund (IMF) early and it's back on track. (11)

look down on PHRASE VERB
To look down on someone means to consider

that person to be inferior or unimportant, usually when this is not true.

EX The class system of the Joseon era has supposedly disappeared, but there still exists a tendency to look down on merchants even in capitalistic Korean society. (160)

meanwhile ADV
Meanwhile means while a particular thing is happening or at the same time.

EX Meanwhile, the Koreans are the most passionate people in the world when it comes to education. (113)

mediate VERB
If someone mediates between two groups of people, or mediates an agreement between them, they try to settle an argument between them by talking to both groups and trying to find things that they can both agree to.

EX This figure would mediate disputes. (34)

negotiation N-VAR
Negotiations are formal discussions between people who have different aims or intentions, especially in business or politics, during which they try to reach an agreement.

EX South Korea has adopted an engagement policy to bring North Korea to the negotiation table in order to gain its trust and avoid the risk of war. (231)

nostalgic ADJ
Nostalgic things cause you to think affectionately about the past.

EX This pride is not just dreamy nostalgic reflections of China's glorious yesteryears. (30)

obligation N-VAR
If you have an obligation to do something, it is your duty to do that thing.

EX In such an atmosphere, instead of looking to fulfill their societal duties and obligations, it is easy for them to look for only personal gains. (163)

obsession N-VAR
If you say that someone has an obsession with a person or thing, you think they are spending too much time thinking about that person or thing.

EX It is a product of the obsession of the Koreans to not fall behind their neighbors. (117)

obstacle N-COUNT
An obstacle is an object that makes it difficult for you to go where you want to go, because it is in your way.

EX It has been an obstacle to national harmony and progress. (134)

obvious ADJ
If something is obvious, it is easy to see or understand.

EX Against such a backdrop, it is obvious what the North Korean regime has in mind. (224)

on purpose PHRASE
If you do something on purpose, you do it intentionally.

EX Hey! Did I do that on purpose? (38)

orthodoxy N-VAR
An orthodoxy is an accepted view about something.

EX This exemplifies how important the Koreans consider orthodoxy and legitimacy. (71)

passion N-UNCOUNT
Passion is extreme compelling emotion or intense emotional drive or excitement.
> **EX** Thus, the Korean parents' passion for education grew fiercer, to say the least. (166)

payback N-COUNT
You can use payback to refer to the profit or benefit that you obtain from something that you have spent money, time, or effort on. Payback also refers to the act of taking revenge.
> **EX** In Korea, however, a shift in political power always brought about some form of political payback. (154)

peculiar ADJ
If you describe someone or something as peculiar, you think that they are strange or unusual, sometimes in an unpleasant way. Peculiar also refers to something that is unique.
> **EX** In fact, the many traits represented by choong are common traits peculiar to people of peninsular countries. (51)

persecute VERB
If someone is persecuted, they are treated cruelly and unfairly, often because of their race or beliefs.
> **EX** Its purpose was to preserve the security of the new regime by persecuting opposition forces as anti-state organizations. (220)

perspective N-COUNT
A particular perspective is a particular way of thinking about something, especially one that is influenced by your beliefs or experiences.
> **EX** From the perspective of sheer size, the South Korean military is no match for the North Korean military. (218)

picky ADJ
Someone who is picky is difficult to please and only likes a small range of things.
> **EX** If the Koreans had been picky about the working conditions, as were workers in more developed countries, they never would have succeeded. (151)

possess VERB
If you possess something, you have it or own it.
> **EX** Like other aspects of Korean society, Korean politics also possesses a degree of extremity that can be hardly found anywhere else in the world. (100)

pour VERB
If you pour a liquid or other substance, you make it flow steadily out of a container by holding the container at an angle. It also means to send forth, produce, express or utter copiously, as if in a stream or flood.
> **EX** After unification, West Germany poured astronomical sums of money into the reconstruction of East Germany. (227)

predicament N-COUNT
If you are in a predicament, you are in an unpleasant situation that is difficult to get out of.
> **EX** Poverty-stricken people often lack the desire and will to overcome their predicament. (157)

prerequisite N-COUNT
If one thing is a prerequisite for another, it must happen or exist before the other thing is possible.
> **EX** However, for most people, education was a prerequisite to success.(167)

prestigious ADJ
A prestigious institution, job, or activity is respected and admired by people.
> **EX** No longer existing now, there used to be a number of prestigious high schools that everyone aspired to attend. (74)

prevail VERB
If a proposal, principle, or opinion prevails, it gains influence or is accepted, often after a struggle or argument.
> **EX** It can be traced to the community spirit that prevailed in Korean society. (126)

principle N-VAR
A principle is a general belief that you have about the way you should behave, which influences your behavior.
> **EX** However, this tenacious spirit often results in the disregard of formal procedures and principles. (153)

priority N-COUNT
If something is a priority, it is the most important thing you have to do or deal with, or must be done or dealt with before everything else you have to do.
> **EX** The government has always emphasized education as its most important priority. (164)

procedure N-VAR
A procedure is a way of doing something, especially the usual or correct way.
> **EX** All processes for unification must be undertaken in accordance with democratic principles and procedures. (212)

proclaim VERB
If people proclaim something, they formally make it known to the public.
> **EX** We proclaim the German Second Reich! (106)

prosperous ADJ
Prosperous people, places, and economies are rich and successful.
> **EX** And they did not become prosperous and powerful nations overnight. (105)

provoke VERB
If you provoke someone, you deliberately annoy them and try to make them behave aggressively.
> **EX** It is important to not provoke the sensitive North Korean regime. (234)

pursuit N-UNCOUNT
Your pursuit of something is your attempt at achieving it. If you do something in pursuit of a particular result, you do it in order to achieve that result.
> **EX** He devoted his life to the pursuit of learning. (54)

qualified ADJ
Someone who is qualified has passed the examinations that they need to pass in order to work in a particular profession.
> **EX** Isn't it obvious that countries with a lot of talented and qualified people are going to be well off? (164)

recession N-VAR
A recession is a period when the economy of a country is doing badly, for example because industry is producing less and more people are becoming unemployed.
> **EX** On the other hand, Japan, which was setting its sight on overtaking America as the world's number one economic power, slipped into a deep recession in the 1990s. (189)

red tape N-UNCOUNT
You refer to official rules and procedures as red tape when they seem unnecessary and cause delay.
> **EX** Why do you think there're all the red tape and the frequent government audits? (162)

reform N-VAR
Reform consists of changes and improvements

to a law, social system, or institution.

EX Park desired to rule forever in the name of national reform. (176)

refuge N-UNCOUNT

If you take refuge somewhere, you try to protect yourself from physical harm by going there.

EX If they felt they could resist no more, the royal family and all the subjects of the court would seek refuge at a safe place (122)

regardless of PREP-PHRASE

If something happens regardless of something else, it is not affected or influenced at all by that other thing.

EX Regardless of how close two friends may be, you'll rarely see them hug. (39)

remnant N-COUNT

The remnants of something are small parts of it that are left over when the main part has disappeared or been destroyed.

EX Remnants of this need for legitimacy and orthodoxy can still be found in Korea. (73)

reparation N-UNCOUNT

Reparations are sums of money that are paid after a war by the defeated country for the damage and injuries it caused in other countries.

EX The government diverted the reparation payments made by Japan for construction costs. (152)

representative N-COUNT

A representative is a person or thing that represents another or others.

EX The representative cases of miraculous economic recoveries have to be the losers of World War II. (105)

reputation N-COUNT

To have a reputation for something means to be known or remembered for it.

EX We'd consider him a shameless person with thick skin who doesn't care about his reputation. (129)

responsible ADJ

If someone or something is responsible for a particular event or situation, they are the cause of it or they can be blamed for it.

EX The federal government is responsible for foreign affairs, national defense and national economic policy. (215)

revision N-VAR

To make a revision of something that is written or something that has been decided means to make changes to it in order to improve it, make it more modern, or make it more suitable for a particular purpose.

EX The Japanese leave a lot of room for change, making practical revisions to suit their needs. (75)

sacrifice VERB

If you sacrifice something that is valuable or important, you give it up, usually to obtain something else for yourself or for other people.

EX Armed with the 'hungry spirit,' these youths studied diligently, vowing to repay the sacrifice made by their parents. (165)

scrutinize VERB

If you scrutinize something, you examine it very carefully, often to find out some information from it or about it.

EX Look how rigorously people even scrutinize the pedigree of dogs! (71)

senior citizen N-COUNT

A senior citizen is an older person who has retired or receives an old age pension.

EX The level of respect for senior citizens and teachers in Korea continues to deteriorate. (198)

significant ADJ
A significant amount or effect is large enough to be important or affect a situation to a noticeable degree.
EX Accordingly, South Korea's policy on North Korea also underwent a significant change. (211)

skeptical ADJ
If you are skeptical about something, you have doubts about it.
EX In this light, many people today still look at businessmen with a skeptical eye. (162)

skyrocket VERB
If prices or amounts skyrocket, they suddenly increase by a very large amount.
EX As the number of colleges skyrocketed, the gap between prestigious and nonprestigious colleges widened. (168)

sovereignty N-UNCOUNT
Sovereignty is the power that a country has to govern itself or another country or state.
EX Under this arrangement, the South and North Korean governments would, for the time being, maintain their sovereignty. (213)

spacious ADJ
A spacious room or other place is large in size or area, so that you can move around freely in it.
EX Having seen the wide and spacious roads in America, they predicted that one day Korea would also be flooded with automobiles. (185)

spread VERB
If you spread something somewhere, you open it out or arrange it over a place or surface, so that all of it can be seen or used easily.
EX But no other place in the world has apartment complexes spread across the country like wallpaper. (63)

squeeze VERB
If you squeeze something, you press it firmly, usually with your hands. It also means to threaten or intimidate in order to obtain a favor, money or action.
EX So its strategy is to squeeze as much money as it can from South Korea. (225)

stir VERB
If a particular memory, feeling, or mood stirs or is stirred in you, you begin to think about it or feel it.
EX In this 'everything's peachy when we're all equal' way of life, trouble stirs not only when one moves ahead, but also when one falls behind (128)

strictly ADV
You use strictly to emphasize that something is of one particular type, or intended for one particular thing or person, rather than any other.
EX Even within a community, the Japanese strictly observe the boundaries of others. (130)

struggle VERB
If you struggle to do something, you try hard to do it, even though other people or things may be making it difficult for you to succeed. It also means a war, fight, conflict, or contest of any kind.
EX The Joseon court paid little attention to foreign affairs, as it was preoccupied with domestic power struggles. (123)

stubborn ADJ
Someone who is stubborn or who behaves in a stubborn way is determined to do what they want and is very unwilling to change their mind.
EX There was no choice but to be stubborn. (45)

submit VERB
If you submit to something, you unwillingly allow something to be done to you, or you do what someone wants, for example, because

you are not powerful enough to resist.

EX Border countries like Korea were forced to submit to China. (19)

sufficient ADJ

If something is sufficient for a particular purpose, there is enough of it for the purpose.

EX Only then would one have accumulated sufficient direct and indirect experience that fuels creativity. (172)

suitable ADJ

Someone or something that is suitable for a particular purpose or occasion is right or acceptable for it.

EX The Japanese modified what belonged to others, making it suitable for themselves. (75)

suppress VERB

If someone in authority suppresses an activity, they prevent it from continuing, by using force or making it illegal.

EX As Catholicism started to gain a larger following, however, during the 19th century, the government started to suppress it. (88)

surrender VERB

If you surrender, you stop fighting or resisting someone and agree that you have been beaten.

EX We'll never surrender to these foreign mongrels! (122)

surveillance N-UNCOUNT

Surveillance is the careful watching of someone, especially by an organization such as the police or the army.

EX A secret police force keeps the people under constant surveillance. (93)

suspicious ADJ

If you are suspicious of someone or something, you do not trust them, and are careful when dealing with them.

EX It would just make North Korea more suspicious

and wary. (232)

sweep VERB

If you sweep an area of floor or ground, you push dirt or rubbish off it using a brush with a long handle. It also means to move across or through swiftly or with great intensity.

EX Education was the only way to succeed - this education fever swept through the country. (114)

take into account PHRASE

If you take something into account, or take account of something, you consider it when you are thinking about a situation or deciding what to do.

EX We're only taking into account the 50 high-income nations in our comparisons! (12)

take over PHRASE VERB

If you take over a job or role or if you take over, you assume management or possession of or responsibility for something.

EX The signs have taken over. (64)

take the initiative PHRASE

If you take the initiative in a situation, you are the first person to act, and are therefore able to control the situation.

EX In the same light, they like to take the initiative and become the leader of the group. (195)

temporary ADJ

Something that is temporary lasts for only a limited time.

EX Korea's probably the only country in the world that places temporary toilets along the congested parts of the highways. (67)

trait N-COUNT

A trait is a particular characteristic, quality, or tendency that someone or something has.

EX It's a trait foreigners have a hard time understanding. (69)

transcend VERB
Something that transcends normal limits or boundaries goes beyond them, because it is more significant than them.

EX In the West, age, status and generation gaps can be transcended in establishing friendships. (79)

transition N-VAR
Transition is the process in which something changes from one state to another.

EX In 1998, Kim Dae Jung succeeded in bringing about the first transition in power between civilian governments in the history of the Republic of Korea. (179)

transparent ADJ
You use transparent to describe a statement or action that is open and free from guile and that you think will not deceive people.

EX A transparent form of capitalism must be established in society. (163)

treaty N-COUNT
A treaty is a written agreement between countries in which they agree to do a particular thing or to help each other.

EX To this date, South and North Korea have failed to sign a peace treaty. (206)

tremble VERB
If you tremble, you shake slightly because you are frightened or cold.

EX Trembling with fear from the constant horrors of a seemingly endless war... (138)

undergo VERB
To undergo something is to endure, sustain or suffer that thing.

EX Then in the 1990s, the world economy underwent a turbulent change. (189)

unification N-UNCOUNT
Unification is the process by which two or more countries join together and become one country.

EX What would be the most ardent wish of the Koreans? It would be the unification of South and North Korea. (206)

unnecessary ADJ
If you describe something as unnecessary, you mean that it is not needed or does not have to be done, and is undesirable.

EX May people live in their hometowns, making it unnecessary for them to go very far during the holidays. (68)

unprecedented ADJ
If something is unprecedented, it has never happened before.

EX ···due to the impact of the Asian financial crisis··· South Korea sets record fall in unprecedented time! (11)

upper hand PHRASE
If you have the upper hand in a situation, you have more power than the other people involved and can make decisions about what happens.

EX Those with new and creative ideas will have the upper hand in competition. (171)

variable N-COUNT
A variable is a factor that can change in quality, quantity, or size, which you have to take into account in a situation.

EX So variables like a country's geographical location, history and culture affect politics. (99)

vice versa PHRASE

Vice versa is used to indicate that the reverse of what you have said is true. For example 'women may bring their husbands with them, and vice versa' means that men may also bring their wives with them.

EX Thus, the two Koreas are yet to have a meeting of the minds on even the most basic step to unification··· So the South insists on pursuing unification in accordance with its plan and vice versa. (210)

victim N-COUNT

A victim is someone who has been hurt or killed.

EX After having endured colonization, war, revolutions, coup d'états and dictatorships during the 20th century, the Koreans cannot erase the thought that they have been victims. (144)

wage N-COUNT

Someone's wages are the amount of money that is regularly paid to them for the work that they do.

EX They endured pitifully low wages, long working hours and poor working conditions··· (177)

witness VERB

If you witness something, you see it happen.

EX Foreigners drop their jaws at this sight that can be witnessed only in Korea. (66)

Adenauer · 199
Admiral Nelson · 200
Admiral Perry · 108
Admiral Yi Sun-shin · 202, 203
agassi · 81
Ahn Chung-gun · 202
'all for one and one for all' mentality · 87
Amaterasu-O-mi-kami · 15, 90
animism · 90
Anti-Communism Law · 219
April 19th Revolution (Student Uprising) · 100, 139
artisan spirit · 187
Asian financial crisis · 111
Asian Games, 1986 · 144, 197
atomic bomb · 109

baekbu · 80
baekjong · 161
bakufu · 35, 36, 53
Balkan peninsula · 44, 59, 60
Brandt, Willy · 199, 233
BT (biotechnology) · 189
bubble economy · 184
Buddhism · 15, 21, 88, 92
Buddhist · 91
bulgogi · 85
Busan · 124
bushi · 36, 52, 53
bushido · 52, 53

caste system · 161
Catholicism · 88
Ceausescu, Nicolae · 94, 95
chaebol · 93, 96, 187
Chiang Kai Shek · 201
Chinese characters · 75, 76, 78
Ching (Dynasty) · 18, 201
Choi Kyu Ha · 101
chon (degrees of kinship) · 82
choong (mentality) · 45, 46, 47, 49, 50, 51, 55, 68, 203, 210

Christianity · 88, 89
Chun Doo Hwan · 101, 179
Chung Ju Young · 167
Churchill, Winston · 200
chusok · 67
Cold War · 206, 211
communism · 48, 93
Communist Party · 212, 217, 220
Confucian society · 80, 115
Confucian traditions · 79
Confucian, Confucianism · 14, 72, 88, 91, 92, 162, 197
Confucius · 14, 46, 53
Constitution of Seventeen Articles · 34
cosmopolitanism · 19
Cultural Revolution · 31, 94

daegongmusa · 46
dangsuk · 80
de Gaulle, Charles · 199
digital revolution · 189
doryeonnim · 81
double-your-income campaign · 186
Duke of Wellington · 200
dure · 126

East Germany · 210, 227
Easter season · 67
Eastern European Bloc · 211, 223
economies of scale · 187
Edo period · 53
education fever · 164, 165, 173, 174
Emmanuele II, Vittorio · 200
Emperor Qin Shi Huangdi · 25
Engels, Friedrich · 31
eonni · 81
Erhard · 199
EU · 107
examination hell · 115
external-force-driven division · 208

faction politics · 103
Franco-German War · 106
French Revolution · 100
Fukuzawa Yukichi · 201

galbi · 85
Gandhi · 200
Ganghwado · 120
Garibaldi, Giuseppe · 200
genealogy · 70
globalization · 170, 189
GNP · 112
gochujang · 85
Gojoseon · 120
Gold Rush · 149
Goryeo Dynasty (Koryo) · 20, 77, 207
Great Depression · 109
gukga baengnyeonjidaegye · 164
guwon · 88
gwageo · 113
Gyeonggi Province · 215
gyunjeom · 49

hagwon · 116
Han (Dynasty) · 19
Han culture · 19, 29, 56
Han River · 124, 184
han (sorrow) · 146
Hangeul · 16, 73
Hegel · 30
Hideyoshi invasions · 86
Hong Gil-dong Jeon · 73
honne · 38, 57
Hoxha, Enver · 94
hungry spirit · 156, 158, 159, 160, 163, 165
hyeongnim · 81
hyeongsunim · 81
Hyundai Group · 167
hyung · 81

internal-conflict-driven division · 208
International Monetary Fund (IMF) · 11, 179
Iron Chancellor Bismarck · 106
Islam · 88
Israel kibbutz · 126
IT (information technology) · 189
Ito Hirobumi · 202

Japanese annexation of Korea · 135
Japanese occupation of Korea · 88
Japanese-American · 149
Jefferson, Thomas · 199
jeong · 131, 132
jeongol · 85
Jews · 156, 161, 162
Jiang Qing · 94
jigae · 85
joong · 46, 47
Joseon Dynasty · 15, 20, 26, 27, 72, 77, 108, 110, 113, 114, 123, 148, 156, 160, 161, 165, 207
Juche · 182
Judo · 116
June 29th Declaration (adoption of direct elec- tions) · 100, 143

Kamakura (Bakufu) · 52
Kennedy, John F. · 199
kikubari · 37
Kim Dae Jung · 179, 180
Kim Il Sung · 94, 95, 103, 138, 181, 182, 210
Kim Jeong-chul · 229
Kim Jong Il · 95, 103, 179
Kim Jong Pil · 102
Kim Ku · 202
Kim Young Sam · 101, 102, 179
kimchi · 63
King Sejong · 72, 202
King Taejong · 72
Kohl, Helmut · 226
Korean Community Unification Plan · 211
Korean democracy · 100

Korean economy · 105
Korean Federation Unification Plan · 215
Korean politics · 98
Korean War · 109, 124, 138, 151, 156, 165, 182, 186, 218
Korean-Americans · 148
Korea's liberation · 88
Krushchev, Nikita · 94

lame duck · 183
lifetime employment system · 187, 192
Los Angeles · 149
Lunar New Year · 67, 68

Manchuria · 136
Manchus · 123
Mao Zedong · 94, 201
Marx, Karl · 31, 89
Matsushita Konosuke · 167
May 16 coup d'etat · 102
May 18th (Gwangju Democratic Movement) · 100
Meiji Restoration · 52, 71, 91, 108, 161, 201
Ming Dynasty · 123
Miracle of the Han River · 155
missile defense system (MD) · 31
Molotov cocktails · 66
Mongol · 18, 20, 21
Mongolians · 119, 122
muban · 113
mudang · 91
munban · 113

Namhansansung · 123
Napoleon · 30
National Security Law · 217, 219, 220
nirvana · 92
Nobel Peace Prize · 102
noblesse oblige · 54
norebang · 69

OECD · 155
oil crisis · 150
Okubo Toshimichi · 201
Olympic Boulevard · 149
one · 23, 27, 28, 29, 32, 42
orthodox, orthodoxy · 50, 51, 59
Ostpolitik · 199, 233

parachute appointments · 190
pariah capitalism · 161, 162, 163
Park Chung Hee · 101, 102, 140, 157, 176, 177, 178, 179, 181, 186
patrimonial *chaebol* capitalism system · 96
PC bang or PC room · 69
per capita GNI (Gross National Income) · 11, 110, 111, 112, 140, 153, 222, 228
phonetic approach, Onyomi · 76
poktanju · 87
polytheistic · 90
Portugal · 89
POSCO · 151, 152
Prince Chungnyeong · 73
Prince of Orange · 200
Prince Shotoku · 15, 34
private education · 116
Protestantism · 88
public education · 116
pumasi · 126

Queen Myeongseong of Joseon · 135

regionalism · 103, 134
Rhee Syng man · 101
Roh Tae Woo · 101, 179
ROK (Republic of Korea) · 116, 179
Roman Empire · 25, 43, 200
Roosevelt, Franklin D. · 199
ROT (Republic of Tutors) · 116

rules of engagement · 80
Russo-Japanese War · 108

Saemaul movement · 140, 196
Saigo Takamori · 202
samgyeopsal · 85
San Francisco · 149
Sega · 41
semantic approach, Kunyomi · 76
seniority system · 187, 192
seonbaenim (Senior) · 134
seonbi · 52, 53, 54, 55
Seoul National University (SNU) · 169, 170, 174
Seoul Olympic Games · 144, 197
shamanism · 91
Shilla Dynasty · 22, 165, 207
Shineuiju · 123
Shinto · 15
Shintoism · 90
shogun · 35, 52
siajubeonim · 81
Sino-JapaneseWar · 27, 108, 135
socialism · 50
soju · 87
solleongtang · 70
South-North Coalition · 213, 214
Soviet Union · 94
Stalin, Joseph · 94
Stalinism · 93, 210, 224
Stalinist state · 224
sumo wrestler · 105
Sun Yat Sen · 201
Sunshine Policy · 231, 232, 233

Tachibana Takashi · 169
Taekwondo · 116
Talmud · 156
Tang Dynasty · 19, 165
Taoism · 14
tatemae · 38, 57
tenno · 35, 201
Thanksgiving holidays · 67, 68
Three Kims · 102

Three Principles of the People · 201
Tibetans · 28
Tokyo Olympic Games · 186
Tokyo University (Tokyo U) · 169, 170
Toynbee, Arnold · 19

Vatican City · 10
Vietnam War · 150

wa · 33, 34, 36, 38, 42, 45
Washington, George · 199
Weber, Max · 31, 161
West Germany · 223
wonjo · 70
World Bank · 11
World Trade Organization (WTO) · 170
World War I · 107, 108
World War II · 99, 105, 107, 119, 186, 199, 206, 208

xenophobia · 57

yangban · 113, 114
yasashii · 37
Yi Seong-gye · 77
Youn Po Son · 101
Yu Kwansoon · 202
yukgyejang · 86
Yun Bong-gil · 202

zaibatsu · 187